TWAYNE'S WORLD AUTHORS SERIES

A Survey of the World's Literature

Sylvia E. Bowman, Indiana University

GENERAL EDITOR

GREECE

Mary P. Gianos, Detroit Institute of Technology

EDITOR

Kostis Palamas

(*TWAS 197*)

TWAYNE'S WORLD AUTHORS SERIES (TWAS)

The purpose of TWAS is to survey the major writers—novelists, dramatists, historians, poets, philosophers. and critics—of the nations of the world. Among the national literatures covered are those of Australia, Canada, China, Eastern Europe, France, Germany, Greece, India, Italy, Japan, Latin America, the Netherlands, New Zealand, Poland, Russia, Scandinavia, Spain, and the African nations, as well as Hebrew, Yiddish and Latin Classical literatures. This survey is complemented by Twayne's United States Authors Series and English Authors Series.

The intent of each volume in these series is to present a critical-analytical study of the works of the writer; to include biographical and historical material that may be necessary for understanding, appreciation, and critical appraisal of the writer; and to present all material in clear, concise English —but not to vitiate the scholarly content of the work by doing so.

Kostis Palamas

By THANASIS MASKALERIS

San Francisco State College

Twayne Publishers, Inc.   : :   New York

To John P. Anton —
Hellenist, inspirer, friend

Contents

Preface

Kostis Palamas is one of the greatest poets of modern Greece. In certain respects, he is the greatest. His contribution to modern Greek literature is twofold. He wrote the richest poetry of his times, much of which is also the most heightened and the most beautiful. At the same time Palamas contributed more than any other writer to the establishment of the vernacular idiom as the literary language of modern Greece. This second achievement was of vast importance not only for Greek literature but for the entire life of the nation. During his long and immensely productive life, especially during the half century from 1880 to 1930, he dominated the literary and intellectual life of Greece as her supreme poet and cultural leader.

Because of Palamas's deep and diverse involvement in the life of his people, it is necessary, particularly in an introductory study such as the present one, to include an examination of the intellectual and sociopolitical conditions in which he lived, with special emphasis on the language problem. Thus it seemed sound to combine biography, cultural history, and literary criticism.

The work of Palamas makes up an immense body and is of every possible genre and mode—lyrical, epic, and dramatic compositions; literary criticism, essays on innumerable subjects and problems of the Greek and the European cultures; a vast correspondence. The criticism of the work of Palamas is also voluminous. The present study of the poet is often guided by his outstanding critics and is heavily indebted to them, particularly to A. Karandonis, I. M. Panayotopoulos, K. Tsatsos, E. Hourmouzios, and A. Doxas.

There are other debts which I wish to acknowledge. The help of George Katsimbalis is always inestimable. With an uncanny divining power as to timing, "the Colossus of Maroussi" supplied much needed material, almost always without my requesting it. And I must confess that the shadow of Katsimbalis was both an inspiration and a source of awe to me: how can a writer measure up to Katsimbalis's epic feelings about modern Greek poetry, particularly when writing about his divine Palamas?

I am especially grateful to my editor, Professor Mary P. Gianos for much practical advice and aid, and for her abounding patience. To the Committee on Comparative Literature of Indiana University I wish to express my appreciation and gratitude for approval and encouragement in writing my master's thesis on Palamas many years ago, particularly to Professor Norbert Fuerst, my inspiring teacher of modern poetry who patiently acquainted himself with Palamas through translations in several languages. Finally I wish to express my gratitude to Professor John P. Anton, the eminent Classical and modern Hellenist, for his inspiration in my studies of Greek poetry and the spirit of Hellenism, and for his generous aid with numerous problems encountered in completing the manuscript.

I wish to also thank Harvard University Press for permission to quote from A. Phoutrides' translations of Palamas and to numerous Greek writers and publishers for permission to quote critical material.

Thanasis Maskaleris

San Francisco State College

Chronology

1929   *The Cycle of the Quatrains.*
1930   *Music Twice Tuned.* Elected president of the Greek Academy.
1931   *Wanderings and Salutations.*
1935   *The Nights of Phemios.*
1943   Dies on February 27. Mass funeral in Athens on the following day.
1944   *Evening Fire,* posthumous poems.

CHAPTER 1

His Early Life and Times

P ALAMAS THE poet emerged with the Generation of 1880, a group of writers who shaped the richest period of modern Greek literature. The social, intellectual, and creative efforts of these writers were animated by the conviction that the only idiom capable of creating a significant literature was the demotic *(demotiké)*, the spoken tongue of the time. Their achievement was the culmination of a long struggle which paralleled the struggles of the Greek people for liberty and, after the War of Independence (1821–29), for political and social organization. In a wider sense, the Generation of 1880 sought a synthesis of the present with the entire Greek past, the shaping and defining of a new Hellenic culture. In this far-ranging movement of reform and regeneration, Palamas was the leading figure, both as an original poet and as a fighter for the establishment of the demotic.

I Childhood and Adolescence

Kostis (Constantine) Palamas was born on January 13, 1859, in Patras, a town of the Peloponnese at the western entrance of the Corinthian Gulf. He was the fourth child of Michael I. Palamas, a judge, and Penelope K. Petala from the island of Ithaka. The birth, infancy, and early childhood of Palamas are surrounded by certain unusual events which had profound effects on his psychic development.[1] Of the three children born before Kostis, two had died. According to local superstition the next child, if male, would also die. Palamas's mother lived in great anxiety and fear when she was pregnant with Kostis. When he was born she was terrified. Additional superstitious fears seized her when she noticed that her newborn son looked remarkably like his father, for "Charon loves the male child that resembles his father." And, to add to these terrible omens, Kostis was born on the thirteenth day of the month. The only way to save their child, the parents thought, was to trick Death into believing that Kostis was a girl.

So they immediately pierced one of the infant's ears and attached a golden earring to it, the gold for which was obtained from forty young, newly wedded women. The earring was to signify his betrothal to life. They also let Kostis's hair grow long and later dressed him in skirts. And they explained to him the significance of the ring as soon as he began to understand the world around him.

Several years later, in a fight with another boy, little Kostis lost his earring. He looked for it desperately but never found it. As a result a deep terror seized him, causing a trauma from which he never recovered, as his later writings clearly testify. When he was a grown man, in his fullest poetic power, he gave dramatic expression to this experience in his poem "The Ring":

> My mother planned a wedding feast for me
> And chose me for a wife a Nereid,
> A tender flower of beauty and of faith.
> My mother wished to wed me with thy charms,
> O Fairy Life, thou first of Nereids!
> And hastily she goes to seek advice,
> Begging for gold from every sorceress
> And powerful witch, and gold from forty brides
> Whose wedding crowns are fresh upon their brows;
> And making with the gold a ring enchanted,
> She puts it on my finger and she binds
> With golden bond my youthful human flesh
> To the strange Fairy—how strange a wedding ring!
>
> I was the boy that always older grew
> With the transporting passion of a pair
> Betrothed who, lured by longing, countenance
> Their wedding moment as an endless feast
> Upon a bridal bed of lily white.
> The boy I was that always older grew
> Gold-bound with Life, the Fairy conqueress;
> The boy I was that always older grew
> With love and thirst unquenchable for Life;
>
> . . . .
>
> But then, one day,—I know not whence and how—
> Upon a shore of sunburned sands, the hour
> Of early evening saddened with dark clouds,
> I wrestled with a strange black boy new-come,
> Risen to life from the great sea's abyss;

became objects of his erotic imagination in an endless succession of adoration-desire and "abandonment." Even the angels inside the churches stirred him when he was a child, he writes with extreme candor, because they were painted like beautiful women.[6]

In 1875 Palamas went to Athens to attend the University School of Law. In contrast to provincial Missolonghi, the capital was an exciting, even overwhelming, megalopolis. But young Palamas was well prepared for it, at least intellectually. Through his readings he had thoroughly acquainted himself with the literary situation, the main currents and personalities in the intellectual and political arenas. And he sought eagerly to take a direct look at the writers and artistic circles that his taste and admiration singled out. Before continuing, however, with Palamas's life and poetic development in Athens, it seems best to examine the language problem in Greece and look at the conditions into which Palamas came upon his arrival in Athens.

II *The Language Problem and the Demotic Tradition*

The "language question" is not a new or recent problem in the history of Greek letters. It is as old as Hellenistic Greek. Since Hellenistic times, two branches of the Greek language have existed side by side, always changing but always in conflict with one another. One was the archaic idiom, later called *logia* (learned) or *katharevousa* (purist). The other was the vernacular of each period, which in recent times has been called demotic *(demotiké)*. The first always tended to maintain the forms of the Attic dialect of Classical Greek and was used by the educated Greeks of each period. It was employed universally for written communication. The second idiom originated as the *koine*, or common language, of the Hellenistic Age. It evolved from the Attic through grammatical, phonetic, and morphological simplifications and gradually developed into the present form of spoken Greek. Plutarch, Lucian, and the Gospel writers used the *koine* in their writings, much to the irritation of their atticizing contemporaries. A destructive bilingualism has plagued Greek letters ever since. After the Athenian Golden Age, the Attic never succeeded in becoming a living, spoken idiom again. The vernacular, on the other hand, never became a written idiom to a significant extent until the nineteenth century. Between these two extremes there existed at times an incomplete synthesis, a mixed idiom which was never capable of solving the language problem.

The Church Fathers, unlike the Gospel writers, steered away from the vernacular of their times and used more archaic forms. And the

Church, with its powerful influence on Byzantine and post-Byzantine Greek life, always adhered to the *logia* tradition which in recent times led to the dominance of the purist idiom. Under these conditions the vernacular was continuously ignored by the educated, and consequently few writings in it have survived. As Byzantium began to decline, however, the demotic idiom gained some ground. Recent studies on Byzantine literature have revealed an outstanding epic production dated between the tenth and thirteenth centuries. The most famous of the demotic epics of this period forms the cycle of Digenis Akritas, named after the legendary hero-guard of the empire's frontiers. Significantly, many of these epic poems were rewritten by contemporary Attic imitators.

With the fall of Byzantium, the scene of literary activity moved to the islands. Crete became the most important literary center of the post-Byzantine period. And it was here that a very important contact between Greece and the West took place. Although subjected to Venetian rule from the beginning of the thirteenth century to 1669, Crete produced an important literature under strong Western influences. But what is most relevant for this study is the progress of the Cretans in the use of the demotic. Their highly developed epic, lyric, and dramatic compositions showed the inherent strength of the spoken idiom as a literary vehicle. Two of the outstanding works of the period are *The Sacrifice of Abraham* (1635), a religious drama of unknown authorship, and *Erotokritos* (1669), a long epic romance by Vicentio Kornaros. These and other Cretan works became cornerstones for later demotic writing.

The poetry of the post-Byzantine period sprang from direct contact with the folk language and life. A relative absence of scholarly preoccupations characterized the times. On the mainland and the islands under Turkish rule, it was the folk song that carried and expressed the tradition. The fate of the enslaved Greeks, their sufferings and aspirations, found expression in their songs. The people were the true poets and Palamas himself was later to dedicate some of his works "to the people, the greatest poet."

In the nineteenth century, the contributions of the folk tradition to poetry was overwhelming. Most poets drew their inspiration and material from it, and since the War of Independence poetry has been organically related to almost every aspect of Greek life. The revival of the folk tradition in the last century was a part of the synthesis with the past. The folksong *(demotiko tragoudi)* had preserved and unified certain elements of Hellenic life and culture; it contained the music and the rhythms which had been part of the activities and spirit of the Greeks for many centuries. That certain folk songs today may have had their origins in ancient Greece is not very surprising if one considers that many regions of Greece, particularly mountainous localities and small islands, were closed areas as far as communication and cultural assimilation were concerned. The "repetition of the kind" in such localities has gone on uninterrupted. Through the centuries each generation greeted the newborn or lamented the dead with the same songs, delivered from mouth to mouth, from ancestor to progeny. In some folk songs of today the idea of death, for example, is still the same as it was in ancient times. Death is a physical struggle with Charon, and it means the loss of the pleasures of the earth and the fervor of living. Notions of paradise and hell are absent, a fact which shows that "the Christian faith has not penetrated the eschatology of the folk song."[7]

A predominant type of folk song during the Turkish occupation was the klephtic song. It was created and sung by the klephts, the mountaineer guerrillas who fought the Turks; in it the hope for freedom lived and spread among the enslaved Greeks. The klephtic songs are short, vigorous ballads characterized by simplicity of feeling and delight in nature. Their patriotic content blends with a tone of wildness which was characteristic of the life and surrounding of the klephts. But there is also delicate emotion in many of them. The klephts were at the same time heroes and poets, living their poems as well as composing them. It is primarily from this stream of the demotic song and the folk tradition in general that Neo-Hellenic poetry sprang.

After the Cretan renaissance the most significant development in the demotic revival took place on the Ionian Islands, which had also fallen under Venetian rule. The rich literary activity of the Ionian writers culminated in the work of Dionysios Solomos (1798–1857). Born in Zakynthos (Zante) but educated in Italy, Solomos wrote his first poems in Italian. He was influenced by Romanticism, by German Idealism and, in matters of language, by the French Enlightenment. At the age of twenty he returned to Greece possessed by the idea of becoming the Dante of Greece. He did become a great poet–the first great poet in the demotic–and the singer of liberty that was being born simultaneously with his poems.

Before the appearance of Solomos on the literary scene, Adamantios Korais (1748–1833) had attempted to indroduce a mid-course idiom as the alternative to bilingualism. But his attempt failed; national literature was to be based entirely on the living, demotic language. Solomos was the first poet to succeed in this inevitable course, proving at the same time that a language cannot be corrected through compromise.

In his study of Solomos, the English critic Romilly Jenkins writes:

The task of Solomos, therefore, was analogous to that which confronted other European poets of the Romantic Age. They too had to combat the outworn "poetic diction" of the eighteenth century. They too had to return to the spoken language of the people, and by acute observation of everyday things and a "selection of the real language of men in a state of vivid sensation" restore to the lifeless, bejewelled corpse of poetry its strength, vividness and simplicity.[8]

Only the situation was much worse in Greece, where pedantry and scorn for the living language had lasted for so many centuries. Concerning the effect of Solomos on the language situation, Jenkins writes:

As Dante had freed Italian literature from the curse of Latin and ennobled his native Tuscan speech by his own expert use of it, so Solomos was in later years to fight the use of decayed Byzantinism and rescue and adorn the beggar-maid of the Greek vernacular.[9]

In the life and work of Solomos we feel the closeness between the poet and his people. "I think of nothing but liberty and language," he writes in his *Dialogue*. The Greek people were at the same time fighting for liberty, and, indirectly, for the establishment of their living language. Thus the poetry of this period was both a product of, and a weapon in, their struggle. Solomos was the first great poet of modern Greece who consciously and passionately devoted himself to the development of the demotic, and his work marks the beginning of a national literature. He became the national poet of Greece and his *Hymn to Liberty* the national anthem. Palamas was the poet who continued and completed the synthesis that Solomos had begun.

III *Palamas and the Demotic Movement*

When Palamas came to Athens the literary scene, unlike that of the islands, was completely dominated by the purists. Leading among them were the Phanariots, members of eminent families of Constantinople who had come to Athens after the liberation. The poets of the period, known as the Old Athenian school, had developed their own type of Romanticism colored by Neoclassical ideas. During the fifty years that followed the Independence (1830–80), they unsuccessfully attempted to transplant the ideas of Western European Romanticism which they understood very little into a newborn, unorganized nation. The resulting political Romanticism was even less successful in meeting the particular demands of the national situation. Thus confusion and exaggeration were the chief characteristics of the period.

It is extremely difficult to see clearly the effects of bilingualism unless one has had direct experience with Greek life on all levels or has been a careful student of the social and intellectual history of Greece. To have one language spoken at home—in everyday life—and a different one, of varying difficulty, used at school and in the government, the church, and the newspapers, is to create serious problems leading to confusion and fragmentation in the social body. The imposition of the purist from above, following Independence, made education a very difficult and largely useless task and bred factionalism, obscurantism, and a special kind of cultural and individual schizophrenia. Archaism in language led to an excessive preoccupation with the distant past—and this in a formal, lifeless way—a hopeless bureaucratic structure and excessive rhetoric of little meaning. Bilingualism also contributed to the stratification of Greek society: high language went together with belonging to a higher, more privileged class, while ignorance of it meant a lower place in society. Purism, then, was a crucial factor in the structuring of the new nation and in determining the character of its people and institutions. And many of the problems attendant on the reign of purism in the first half century after Independence have continued to plague Greek national life down to this day.

Palamas and the movement he eventually led came as a reaction against the above conditions and, in literature, against the purist Romantics. Although the enthusiasm and vitality of the writers in Palamas's circle sprang from their contact with the Romantic spirit, their outlook on life and national problems was realistic. They focused attention on the present, and they valued above all else the living forces of the people, deeply aware of the necessity for a complete change in the life of the nation. In the words of Emilios Hourmouzios, one of Palamas's critics:

Palamas manifests himself at the most crucial moment in the life of his nation. It is the time when a future is to be built. It is the moment when the past, with all it has already given and all that it may still give, must be placed on one side of the scale, and on the other the new consciousness that has not yet given anything, that has not marked its path, that dimly sees the future. But the new consciousness sees very clearly that the idols and values of the past are unable to give vitality to the new life. It is a time when relentless decisions and actions are necessary.[10]

From this crossroads Palamas led the way to a new life. His personality filled every phase of the struggle. He redefined and revitalized the lasting values of the Hellenic tradition, presenting them as symbols rather than as rigid norms of life. Above all, he prepared the conditions which enabled the new embryos in the national life to become full-grown realities.

For Palamas and those who shared his convictions, purism was not only the main obstacle to progress but a deadly poison for the national life. Thus in the years around 1880 there was a gathering of forces in the demotic front for the first concentrated attack on the enemy. The beginning was slow and unspectacular, simply the publication of poems in the demotic and articles, invariably written in the purist, presenting the ideology of the demotic movement. But if one considers the fanaticism and hostility of the completely dominant purists, to publish in the demotic was an act of revolutionary defiance. And as the ranks of the demoticists expanded, the wrath of the purists increased in vehemence.

Palamas had written his youthful poems in the purist mode as all his contemporaries had, under the influence of recent and current writings. He even admired some of the leading purist poets. But almost immediately after his arrival in Athens he began to turn away from purism. His earlier admiration for the demotic poets, especially for Solomos and Aristotelis Valaoritis, was now rekindled by the leading exponents of the demotic. The writings of the controversial critic Emmanuel Roidis and, later, an incisive criticism of purism and contemporary institutions by Demetrios Vernardakis, had an immense influence on Palamas during these crucial years of orientation. In 1876, at the age of seventeen, he published his first poem in the demotic, but he continued to write poems in both idioms for several more years. The break with the purist was not clear-cut, however, since he continued to write prose in the purist for many years afterward.

During his first fifteen years in Athens, Palamas moved from an admiration for the demotic tongue to the conviction that it should become the universal language of literature and of the entire national work instead of earning his livelihood through journalistic writing, as he had done until that time. (2) In 1887 Palamas married Maria Valvi, whom he had known since his childhood years in Missolonghi. They had three children: a girl, Nausicaa, and two boys, Leandros and Alkis. The youngest son, Alkis, died in 1898. Thus, during the perilous days of the riots, Palamas risked not only his own safety but that of his family as well. His wife had fled several times from their house with the children for greater safety.

During these days—as in all the years—of strife and danger, Palamas remained at his post as general secretary of the university, courageously doing whatever he could to restore calm and reason. He never went into hiding away from Athens and never retracted anything that he had said or written in defense of the demotic. Without resorting to his opponents' mob-swaying tactics, but with dignity and courage, he continued to fill his leading position at the battlefront both with his presence in the center of the storm and, above all, with his writings.

Two years later, in 1903, even more violent riots broke out in opposition to a scheduled performance by the National Theater of Aeschylus's *Oresteian Trilogy* in a demotic translation. This time Palamas was the central target of the rioters—students, professors, and the stirred populace, who understood the issues pitifully little. He received numerous threats, insults, and humiliations, but again he remained courageous and unyielding. In fact, the harshness of the struggle only strengthened his convictions and gave force and realism to his writing. During his most combative period (1888–1908), he wrote most of his greatest work.

IV *The Early Collections (1886–1900)*

Songs of My Country is the first collection of Palamas's poems in the demotic. It appeared, as mentioned earlier, in 1886. It contained poems written between 1882 and 1885, most of which had been published in magazines. They are love poems, nature poems, and poems based on events of the War of Independence. The spirit of 1821 and the heroic deeds of the revolutionary fighters were rich sources of inspiration for Palamas and a starting point for his lifelong undertaking to relate himself to his ancestors, the present to the recent and the remote past.

The collection was greeted with enthusiasm by the demoticists and with irritation and hostility by the purists. If the purists could have looked below the surface, beyond the language they despised, they would have seen new themes and a new spirit, a realistic preoccupation with the present and the immediate, in complete opposition to their own attitudes and preoccupations. Here Palamas expresses, in a concrete and robust demotic, a palpitating love for Greek nature as he experienced it and a burning concern for the actual Greece that he observed, not the remote, idealized Greece of the old school.

In the poems of this collection Palamas makes extensive use of rhythms, imagery, and themes of folk songs and chants of lamentation, and he succeeds remarkably in clothing his ideas with the common dress of the folk idiom, thus realizing the ideal of Solomos, who wrote: "The difficulty lies in taking sounds of common use and making them express things which are not common, fitting them so that they say what has never been said before, and yet what everybody can feel and understand." With *Songs of My Country* Palamas begins what will become a lifelong task: bringing poetry down to concern itself with the actual conditions of his environment and at the same time elevating the demotic to express the loftiest thoughts and feelings of the poet.

In his next two poetic works, *The Hymn to Athena* (1888) and *The Eyes of My Soul* (1892), Palamas continued to assimilate the past and relate it to present social needs. This assimilation and reevaluation of the past was an attempt to solve a serious problem: the empty love of his contemporaries for the Greek past. The following excerpt from the Introduction to *The Eyes of My Soul* shows his conception of a synthesis of past and present:

With the union of the two antithetical elements, the ancient and the modern, a new art of unspeakable beauty comes forth. If the poet runs back into the past, he seeks in it new significant images, and forms, symbols with which he expresses his thoughts and feelings; feelings and thoughts of the spirit of modern times which are influenced, although he does not suspect it, by the environment. In this union the modern spirit becomes clearer and the old is transformed as the nature of the artistic creation requires, which is not, to be sure, like the work of the photographer or the archaeologist. (*Works* 212–13)

The present is the center of life; its demands must be understood in creating a new art and new values.

In *The Hymn to Athena* and *The Eyes of My Soul*, the language of Palamas has become richer and more effective, a more genuine and better controlled demotic. The somber moods and the musical free verse in *The Eyes of My Soul* indicate the influence of Symbolism. In lyrical emotion, hails *The Grave* as one of the loftiest peaks in Palamas's poetic achievement, precisely because of its lyrical purity.[1 2]

In its unadorned language, simple melodiousness, and richness of folk materials, *The Grave* is almost a traditional song of lament:

>In the journey where
>the black rider leads you
>see that you take nothing
>from his hand.
>
>And if you grow thirsty
>in the lower world
>do not drink the water of forgetfulness,
>my little uprooted mint.
>
>Do not drink it and
>forget us forever,
>but place sign-posts
>to mark your way.
>
>And as you are light,
>tiny like a swallow,
>and the pallikari's arms
>do not weigh on your waist,
>
>see that you out-trick
>the sultan of the night
>to slip secretly away
>and fly to the upper world.
>
>And when you return
>to our desolate home
>become a gentle zephyr
>and a sweet kiss.

(*Works* I, 398)

In 1906, following a visit to the child's grave, Palamas wrote a sequel to *The Grave,* called "The First Logos of the Paradises." This poem, the first part of a projected composition in eight sections, is a vision and contemplation of death in a suprahuman, universal setting.

In *The Greetings to the Sunborn Woman* (1900) the search of Palamas for a new religion centers again on science. In this, as in several subsequent works, science becomes a central theme which finds its fullest expression in *The Dodecalogue of the Gypsy.* For Palamas, science always bathes in beauty and breathes in a metaphysical air. The Sunborn Woman is such a science ideal. She is offspring of the Sun, the source of Truth and Beauty. At the same time, she is a symbol of the new consciousness that was emerging in his times, the new Greek consciousness represented by the demotic revival and the new European consciousness that would rise as the outcome of the battle between metaphysical theocracy and positivism. And Palamas, the torn seeker of harmony, the careful watcher of currents and movements, could not but be attracted by the writings of Herbert Spencer, the harmonizer of the torn age. Spencer presented a bridging compromise by recognizing both the mystical realm of religion and the empirical domain. His theories influenced Palamas strongly by stimulating and directing his oscillating mind. Through the symbol of his Sunborn Woman, Palamas expressed the vision of a world guided by a "composite science," crown of the new consciousness. As Palamas later wrote:

Each power [positivism and idealism] attracts me in a different way. I know that positive science can introduce me to what we call truth when we do not want to play with words. And again comes the metaphysical dream demanding to increase infinitely the depth of my vision. My imagination is stimulated, at the same time and in turns, by the materialist and the transcendental philosophies. I am a singer of monism moving towards some non-material pluralism. *The Sunborn Woman* and "The Ascrean" are manifestations of this tempestuous and tortuous path, of the movement from the formulated knowledge . . . to the divine creation of the metaphysical imagination . . . and vice versa from the second to the first.[13]

Will the new consciousness stop at the idol of science? This is the central question asked in *The Sunborn Woman.* And the poet's answer is a negative one: he and the new art must go beyond science. His faith in a more complete ideal of life expands his horizons and prepares him for a wider vision. A universal humanism is beginning to take shape.

CHAPTER 2

Life Immovable—The Struggle of the Self

LIFE IMMOVABLE marks the beginning of Palamas's second creative period. Published in 1904, it contains poems written during the preceding decade. It is a large collection, diverse in subject matter and prosodic experiments. Its complex lyrical movements reflect Palamas's struggle to master and express his many conflicts and concerns. The work is divided into nine sections, as follows:

1. "Fatherlands"
2. "The Return"
3. "Fragments from the Song of the Sun"
4. "Verses of a Familiar Tune"
5. "The Palm Tree"
6. "A Hundred Voices"
7. "From the Hymns and Songs of Wrath"
8. "From the 'Great Visions' "
9. "A Few More Songs"

"From the 'Great Visions' " contains "The Ascrean" and "The Chains." "Great Visions" and "The Palm Tree" are long compositions, while the remaining sections contain numerous short poems. The whole collection is a song of all life elevated to the harmony and immutability of poetic sublimation. The poet's life, too, becomes "immovable" in the realization of his lyrical passion beyond and above the turmoils of everyday life:

> . . . Away from the market's clatter,
> in the deep shade of plane trees, far away
> by the blood-tinted settings of the suns,
> unconquered, in another land I traveled
> and deep I dug in treasure mines.
>
> ("The Return"—Dedication)

Immutable also, in the midst of all changing things, is the love of the poet for his song.

I *Lyrical Paths*

"Fatherlands" is a group of sonnets about various localities of Greece and other countries. The poet sings of Parnassus and the Nile, of the land of lotus-eaters, and of America:

> . . . in my soul's depths many lands loom:
> some ancient and unchanging like Asia,
>
> others many-minded and daring like Europe;
> despair oppresses me like Africa's black earth;
> I feel a savage Polynesia stirring within me
> and I always follow some Columbian course.
>
> ("Fatherlands" IX)

A feeling of cosmopolitanism overflows in his verse and leads him to an ideal conception of fatherland which goes far beyond his early patriotism. In the following sonnet of this section, the poet's imagination rises to a universal vision of the earth and relates the indestructible elements to man's mortality and to the life of art:

> Fatherlands! Air and earth and fire and water!
> Elements indestructible, beginning
> And end of life, first joy and last of mine!
> You I shall find again when I pass on
>
> To the grave's calm. The people of dreams
> Within me, airlike, unto air shall pass;
> My reason, fire-like, unto lasting fire;
> My passions' craze unto the billows' madness;
>
> Even my dust-born body, unto dust;
> And I shall be again air, earth, fire, water;
> And from the air of dreams, and from the flames
> of thought, and from the flesh that shall be dust,
> And from the passions' sea, ever shall rise
> A breath of sound like a soft lyre's complaint.
>
> ("Fatherlands" XII)

The poems in the following section, "The Return," grew out of the gloomy aftermath of the Greco-Turkish War of 1897. The defeat of the Greeks in this war was a shattering blow to national aspirations, to the hope for recovering large Greek-populated territories from Turkish rule and recapturing the glory of Byzantium. This dream for territorial expansion and regaining old glories, later known as *Megali Idea* (Great Idea), played an important role in the national life for an entire century, until the defeat and massacre of the Greeks in Asia Minor (1922). Palamas's work reflected and often rekindled this burning ideal. Thus in the opening poem of "The Return," he attempts to soothe his suffering Mother (Greece) and to inspire hope in his discouraged countrymen. The poet becomes, once again, "the greatest patriot." But general hopelessness afflicts the poet's heart as well, and the prevailing tone in "The Return" is one of anguish and pressimism, a pessimism that moves from social concern to personal confession, the "poet's own consciousness of hopelessness and degradation."[1]

A glance at Palamas's *Poetics* would illuminate his psychological state during this period, as well as the entire pessimistic vein which runs deep in his life and work. In the section called "The Three Lyricisms," Palamas states: "I have the feeling that I am not one individual; that I am not with one but with many selves."[2] The poet, and man in general Palamas goes on to explain, carries within him three main elements: the individual element, which distinguishes him from others; the topical or social element, which unites him with his society; and the universal element, which makes him one with humanity. Palamas calls his poetry a synthesis of these three elements of awareness. To each of these corresponds a distinct type of lyricism: the lyricism of "I" which expresses the individual, the lyricism of "we" which expresses the social, and the lyricism of "all" which expresses the universal.

In his own work, the lyricism of "we" grows out of his sense of tradition and social consciousness. It is strongly nationalistic and consequently gives rise to love of his country and ancient ancestors. This lyricism of "we" is predominant in the early work of Palamas.

The lyricism of "I" springs from the inner conflicts of the poet. More specifically it seems to rise from the idealistic tendencies of man, but "at bottom is nothing but a physiocratic, pre-Christian—monastic is perhaps the best term—hedonism."[3] After he comes to this realization, Palamas sees himself as a Romantic and speaks of powerful feelings of self-degradation and self-laceration raging in him.

The poet, naturally, suffers from a deep feeling of degradation which becomes increasingly painful as the years pass. And the unfolding of his song, with all its musical variety, is frequently interrupted by the insistent manifestation of a sense of hidden evil. This psychological convulsion, indefinite and inexplainable though it is, leaves the erotic tempest far behind.[4]

The result of this awareness is a helplessness and a sense of inner ruin, which in many poems turn into feverish confession. Several poems in "The Return," particularly "The Ring," "The Madman," and "The Dead," are characteristic of this state of loss:

> A madman haunted my childhood years—
> the sweet, blossoming years of my youth—
> and seizing them he crushed them in his rage
> like tender twigs of purple pomegranate.
>
> . . . .
>
> (And the madman was blood of my blood,
> an ancestral long-forgotten sin
> that, bursting upon me like a vampire,
> snatched from my head the dewy crown of spring.)
>
> ("The Madman")

The third lyricism, the universal, is a synthesis of the first two. It is a search for lofty, universal symbols through which the poet expresses the richness and triumph of life. The patriotic lyricism of "we" Palamas calls "tyrtaism," thus recalling the heroic flame of the ancient poet Tyrtaeus. The lyricism of the tormented ego he calls "Kassianism," a term derived from the name of the Byzantine nun and psalmodist Kassiane, whose famous hymn of sin and repentance Palamas has brilliantly recast in his *The Altars.* Finally, he gives the name "poetic comparatism" to the lyricism of "all." Pessimism is the dominant mood in his "kassianic" lyricism, while an optimism for the future of Greece and of humanity vibrates in his "tyrtaic" and "universal" poems.

In "Fragments from the song of the sun," written in 1899, Palamas once again turns to the gods and heroes of the past, particularly to those of ancient Greece. His imagination raises them into lofty symbols illuminated by a cosmic sun, father and unifier of all. This sun of the "Fragments" is a complex symbol, representing a life-giving source that permeates both the physical universe and the inner world of man. And the poet, one feels, is a humbler counterpart of this mighty sun. "Giants's Shadows," with its two diverse heroes, Ajax the Telamonian and Goethe, indicates Palamas's direction of thought in these poems:

> Like moans of the sea, I hear
> voices emerging from the dark realms.

The shadows of giants shift:
"Who art thou, O Shade? Speak!"
—"I am the Telamonian!
Look! Even in Hades I hold within me
the entire sun that never sets!
Do not weep for me!"
—"And thou? Who art thou?"
—"From the heart of the Teutonic lands
I sprang, a supreme maker of Olympian
worlds. But see how, even here in the depths
of Tartarus, one thirst still
burns my heart—my longing for light!"

The poems in the section entitled "Verses in a Familiar Tune" (1900) mark a return to the simple song and to familiar themes, mostly in the manner of the subjective confession. Among these, "The Paralytic on the River's Bank" is of special significance as a mirror of Palamas's sense of inner ruin.

II *"The Palm Tree"*

In his analysis of "The Palm Tree," one of Palamas's critics writes: "The larger compositions of the poet in *Life Immovable* seem, if viewed from a distance, like a flight from the depths of sorrow to the luminous summit of the ideal." [5] This statement describes perfectly the movement of the poet's imagination in "The Palm Tree." Some humble, blue flowers, growing in the shade of a palm, open their eyes to the world above them, to the gigantic tree:

O Palm Tree, a hand has cast us here;
Was it a hand moved by a cursed Fate;
or by a mind of good intent? Who knows?

. . . .

Is it a destroyer's or a savior's will
that keeps us motionless in your shade?
And is your shade of life or of death?

The blue flowers symbolize man who awakens before the vastness of nature and attempts to discover his identity and destiny. The poet here identifies himself with the blue flowers and lives their longings and agony. The palm tree symbolizes the Absolute. Leandros Palamas, the poet's son, speaks of the Palm Tree-Vegetation, the Palm Tree-Woman, and the Palm Tree-Idea, all three being aspects of the Absolute with which man strives to unite.[6] Another critic writes that "The palm tree symbolizes our ideal which is our love of Life with all its enigmas and secrets. It symbolizes our tendency towards the height which is symbolism."[7] Beyond the differences of opinion among the critics as to what the central theme of the poem is, there is general agreement that the palm itself is a symbol of the Absolute or the Ideal.

Bathed in dew, all the other flowers in the garden are happy; and "each bird dreams it is a nightingale." But the blue flowers are burning with the desire to know; to understand nature and themselves. They represent the sensitive and contemplative human beings. And it is sensitivity that causes their pain, as well as their exaltation: "One, damned, and godlike, dwells in us; and she is Thought!" Palamas frequently speaks of this dual nature of his thought and of his lyrical passion: "And so rises, like an altar to a pantheistic Aphrodite, this two-sided idea inside which live together the soul's Ormuzd and Ahriman: the great personage Whole."[8] This coexistence of good and evil, of joy and pain, in man explains the conflicting sides of the poet's thought and the dialectic pattern that runs through his entire work. The flowers have the noble aspiration to rise in the tranquillity of knowledge and divinity. But they realize that they are destined to remain humble, weak, and unknown in the vast drama of life that unfolds over them: "Everyone saw our surface, none our depths. And so the world glided over us and vanished." The alternately happy and anguished moods, the joyful hymns of love for life and the lamenting chants of the tortured soul, so characteristic of Palamas, are dramatically cast here:

> Who ever thought of it! What fate has ruled
> That from ill-smelling things and worthless stuff
> Should rise things of resplendent green? and from
> Deforming filth, the thrice-pure miracle
> of May and April? Hence things blue and black
> Mingle in us; and in our souls, spread oceans
> And narrow paths; and while our minds converse
> With things sublime, something thrice-base defiles us!

The flowers ask the Sun to "strangle all black dreams" and transform everything into a festival of light and love. The Palm Tree (Idea) is rising to the stars, while the blue flowers remain on earth tasting sorrow, knowing only toil and anguish. But the poet unites the worldly with the divine, the actual with the ideal. And he marvels at the amazing participation of man in both worlds: "Strange was the hour—who can believe it?—when the divine world willed to become Thought and to reveal itself in our mind!" Man can partake of the Ideal, but he can never understand it fully; yet he ceaselessly strives to find the answers, down to the last moment of his life:

> And now toward new mysteries and the unknown dark
> our little lives are ready to depart.
> O Palm, answer us! Alas, before you speak
> the highest word, the waiting hand will strike.

So the blue flowers—each generation of man—will die and no one will notice their passing. Only a circle of light will hover above them to adorn the palm; a "deathless gleam; /and it shall be our thought, and word, and rime!" Man passes, but his song lives on. And with "The Palm Tree," a hymn to the natural and the supernatural world, Palamas has sung one of his greatest songs.

"The Palm Tree" has been compared to Shelley's "The Sensitive Plant,"[9] about which Palamas had read in Taine's *Histoire de la littérature anglaise*. The two poems are similar in setting, basic symbolism, and imagery, but their central ideas are sharply different. What is for Shelley the Lady-Spring, the regenerating power of nature, is for Palamas the Absolute Idea which inspires man to strive toward a higher civilization. Many parallels may be drawn between the two poems, but the final direction of lyrical thought in each shows their essential difference.

From the point of view of form, "The Palm Tree" is one of Palamas's most perfect works. The idea that form and content must be harmoniously blended, which had strongly influenced Palamas, is perhaps more completely realized in this poem than in any other. Here, in a lyrical monologue of three hundred and twelve lines, Palamas's musical use of the thirteen-syllable line is unsurpassed in modern Greek poetry. It is interesting to note also that Palamas gradually abandons conventional symbolism, which is based primarily on mythology, and creates his own private symbols that rise out of his direct contact with nature. "Thus, this final and subconscious symbolism of the poet of 'The Palm Tree' approximates to the spirit of German Romanticism, though it also takes something from the French Symbolist School."[10]

III *"A Hundred Voices"*

The "Hundred Voices" are one hundred short poems without titles, expressing a great variety of impressions, ideas, and conflicts. In Palamas's own words, they are:

one hundred sighs which spring from a single emotion; only the tone of each one is different. But even the most diverse of them belong to one of two large psychological categories: "tyrtaism" and "kassianism," or more simply, *sublimation* and *contrition*—two states that inspire and color not only these hundred poems but my entire poetic work. "The Palm Tree" is a synthesis; in the "Hundred Voices" the synthetic edifice falls to pieces and vanishes.[11]

Elsewhere he writes:

No one realizes that "The Palm Tree," the "Hundred Voices," and "The Ascrean " . . . are one lyrical trilogy. One follows the other, in spite of all their exterior unlikeness, in a symphonic evolution which only a careful analysis, or better *psychoanalysis,* could show. Each poem is the transformation and the completion of the one that precedes.[12]

Moreover, Palamas considers the "Hundred Voices" an example of his "cyclical mania,"[13] a chain of poetic ideas, independent in the various poems of a collection and yet psychologically unified to express an entire life cycle. Many moods and subjects find expression in such poetic cycles. The poet's imagination sweeps from man's burning blood to the "Muse of thought." The prevailing motive in the present "Voices" is the "constant resistance against the forces of evil, and faith in the final triumph of thought."[14] A deep voice resounds in the opening lines:

> Said the great poet: "In all darkness
> the deepest darkness is the soul.
> Man is always a riddle for the woman
> and you, woman, man's eternal sphinx.
> An abyss gapes within me, black law,
> alas! alas! And no one knows my terror.
> No one but I."

(Voice 1)

Palamas laments for his personal misfortunes and those of his people. But no one hears him. The poet is isolated from his people as the blue flowers in "The Palm Tree" were unnoticed by the world around them.

Yet he can look toward the future and hope for the dawn of happier days.

The language ideal resounds in the following lines:

> Word's Nereid, my mother's and my soul's
> Own tongue, a thousand scorns
> Have furrowed your bright face and bent your head;
> Stand up erect; triumphal hymns I sing you!
> And from tomorrow's world, I bring to you
> The message of a victory whose gleam,
> Like a far star's, will after many years
> Come to us here—O tongue
> Of humble Hellas, victor over death.
>
> *(Voice 16)*

This poem was written during the most turbulent days of the language controversy, when Palamas's wrath and his faith in the cause were at a peak.

Palamas's preoccupation with the two antithetical forces that shaped the life of the Greeks—paganism and Christianity—is manifest in "A Hundred Voices." And his faith in the new consciousness is prophetically voiced: "We are neither Christians nor pagans; but we seek to create, out of idol and cross, the new life whose name is still unknown." (*Voice* 53). With word and action he encourages his people to bring forth this new life: "Forward to battle for your gods!" He observes the struggle of his contemporaries as they search for new gods. At times it is a disillusioning struggle of men who do not succeed in their pursuit of truth; of men who remain "outside the metaphysical palaces." At other times science offers new values, created and measured by the law of thought:

> The wise man said to man:
>   "I am a measure new
> And show all human things at a new price and weight;
> I cast all idols down or crush them into dust.
> Yet the destroyer, death, is a creator too.
> I bring you a bridge mightier than Jacob's ladder,
> A bridge I planned and built; and now it stands before you,
> Ready, to lead you from the marshy sea that folds
> A lurid shroud about you to divine Olympus."
>
> *(Voice 67)*

But against the force of reason the poet sets the life of the heart:

> And man made answer to the wise:
> "Crush every idol.
> Over their broken fragments I shall weep and wail;
> though you transform all things, to me they are the same;
> And I shall call them by the same names as before;
>
> . . . .
> I cannot climb where you would lead, nor can I go
> Forward; and like a night bird blinded by the day,
> I beat my wings, wise man, and droop before your light."
>
> $\qquad\qquad\qquad\qquad\qquad\qquad\qquad$ (*Voice* 68)

The poet ends the cycle on a tragic note. He started in the greatest darkness and ends with plucked wings on a "sunless path." But he has struggled for light and for beauty: "I loved you well, O Muse of Thought!" he cries with his last breath. This is his only joy.

Hourmouzios compares Palamas's inner conflicts with those of his milieu and finds that poet and society reflect one another: "Palamas does not assimilate a stable faith, or a straight and definite moral path, but represents wavering, doubt, uncertainty—a road that is frequently crossed by confusing side paths."[15] He mirrors and represents his time: a mixture of pessimism and optimism. Thus, sometimes we hear in his poetry the weak heartbeat of a broken man near death and at other times the vigorous palpitation of new life.

IV   *"The Ascrean"*

"The Ascrean," the last poem of the cyclic trilogy, is the first of the "Great Visions." It is a long poem (655 lines) and one of Palamas's greatest works. In the poet's words:

"The Ascrean" is a very significant step in my creative life. . . . On the manuscript I have scribbled hastily: "Hymen of ancient poetry with the new singer, like the marriage of Helen and Faust." . . . With the "Palm Tree" I had built . . . a tree and a statue with grass and dew around it—not to mention the symbolism. The "Hundred Voices" destroyed the tree, the statue and the dewy grass. The poet felt the pain of this desolation and in order to forget and to console himself in an *illusion* . . . he had to fly to the far horizons and the ideals that uplift him . . . and so the "Ascrean" came as a *regeneration*.[16]

"The Ascrean," as the last poem of the trilogy, is on the whole a positive synthesis that establishes a harmony with the world. It presents a union of poet and nature without the metaphysics of "The Palm Tree." In his *Poetics* Palamas wrote: "My song does not find the ideal patterns of things in the unworldly sphere; my ideal is the worldly."[17] This worldly idealism, an inverted Platonism, is the backbone of "The Ascrean." As the first song of the "Great Visions," on the other hand, "The Ascrean" is a turning point, a move from a psychological and ideological sense of defeat to optimistic visions of the future.

In this poem Hesiod, the poet from Ascra, is the singer. He is the poet of toil in contrast with Homer who "sings in tranquil strains of men, heroes and gods." The preference of Hesiod over Homer shows the realistic preoccupation of Palamas with the actual problems of his time. Furthermore, the poet from Ascra agrees with the psychological make-up of Palamas; their themes and concerns are also similar.

In the opening lines Hesiod, the mortal who died twice, is returning from Hades. He meets the modern poet under an olive tree and addresses him. Then he calls on the "old life-song" to guide him on his poetic journey. As the Ascrean speaks of his life, one recognizes Palamas speaking of his inner self:

> On this primeval land
> my fathers' graceless lives
> knew the constant howling of jackals.
>
> . . . .
>
> I was not nurtured with sweet milk from the Muses' breasts;
> pain and misery were my bitter food.

But one day, the Ascrean met "the nine goddesses" who blessed him with the gift of song, and since that day: "I dream of a tenth Muse among the Muses in a world that still escapes my searching thought." Every great poet seeks to go beyond the limits of his tradition, to create an original poetry, to add depth to the awareness of existence. The "tenth Muse" stands for the poetic achievement beyond this threshold.

The Ascrean then recalls the ages of man through which he journeyed. But in spite of the common tale there are marked differences between Hesiod's and Palamas's handling of the legend.

The ancient poet of the *Works and Days* introduces the legend of the Five Ages in order to illustrate his pessimistic view that man's life was happier in the remotest past and that, with time, crime and woe have been winning the ascendance, culminating in the present age, the unhappiest of them all. . . . He asks us to look on them objectively and accept them as a true report of bygone times, in which we have had no share. Not so with Palamas. With the modern poet of Greece, unity is won through subjectivity. The five ages are not detached from our own lives to the remote past, but they are man's own—at least, the poet's own—experience. The golden age and the silver age, the age of bronze and the age of heroic deeds are just as real parts of our lives as the gloomy age of iron.[18]

By depicting all five ages as experiences of his own, Palamas evokes more vividly the depth and complexity of our age, of contemporary man.

In the golden world the Ascrean poet meets the godlike men who live in tranquillity. They never die but just move from the earth to live forever with the gods on "blessed Olympus." This age is the infancy of humanity when man is happiest, like a child. From here the Ascrean moves to the silver world:

> Where snow-clad forests spread
> Beaten by merciless and glaring moonlight
> That weaves its crowns of pearl
> To crown the head of mortals wrapped in gloom.
>
> . . . .
>
> The shroud of the silver glow reflected wraps
> All things from mind to grass,
> A light that struggles to become a day
> And ever stays at dawn.

This is a twilight world in which man begins to become conscious of himself, to search for his identity. The Ascrean attempts to "free" the inhabitants of the silver world by offering them the fire of the human heart. But the silver people, the "godless race," do not listen to him. The bronze age follows with its "stern violence, hatred, and wrath," a world that is "shaped by the hammer's stroke." The Ascrean remembers the flames that burned his soul: "And my soul, that had served in the workshop of gentle rhythm, was caught and beaten in the whirlpool of brazen flames."

The fourth age is that of the heroes where the might of great men dominates. Here there is enormous strength but no moral purpose. Thebes is the best example of this world of lust and evil: "here, in the hushed hollows, the shameless Satyrs dance. Where are the dreams of deeds, the deeds of dreams?" Here, too, the trumpet of the poet sounds in vain; he is misunderstood and mocked.

In the fifth, the iron age, man is most evil. The Ascrean belongs to this age, and he speaks with the pain of actual experience:

> Sun's frightful ghost, man, breeds and wallows low
> In rotten swamps of life.
> For staining her, Night even curses him,
> Lust-hunter, doer of wrong.
> Crime is lord; violence, mistress; a bitch, the woman.
>
> . . . .
>
> The nights I lived in the dark world of iron,
> Have marred my life, it seems,
> With stains that know no healer's hand, but pierce
> And creep within, sin-breeding.

After telling of the Ascrean's journey through the five ages of man, Palamas relates the myth of Pandora. According to Hesiod, Pandora was given by the gods to make man's life futile and difficult. For Palamas, however, Pandora, more specifically, symbolizes physical passion in its consuming and binding aspects:

> Unbridled passion dragged me on, a rider,
> through the narrow paths, the slippery ravines.
>
> . . . .
>
> The knife of mighty love stabbed me
> and painfully I perished in my thirst.
> I died and passed into the icy realms
> to drink the water of forgetfulness.

But passion is both destroyer and exalter of man. From his symbolic death the poet is awakened to self-knowledge and a more harmonious relation with the world. At this point Palamas deviates completely from the Hesiodic myth. In the underworld the Ascrean meets Persephone, "double and one, death's queen, life's maidenhood." After he sings of the upper world and she speaks to him of the mysteries of life and death, a new kind of love awakens in the poet's soul for Persephone: "And I love you because only you live; the rest around you are shades—shades that exist no more or wait to be born." Persephone is a creation with the familiar antithetical nature: she is both the source of life and the queen of death. She inspires the poet with a love which finds beauty and divinity in all things and "prays one prayer to all in the same temple of tranquility." Moved by the poet's love for her and by the beauty of life, Persephone longs to return to the upper world. She asks the poet to accompany her on the spring ascent and, with his art, help her to regenerate the earth.

With his return to the earth the Ascrean ends his journey, which was a journey into his soul. Having acquired self-knowledge, he is now able to understand the world objectively. He turns to the modern Greek poet, his "flesh and heir," and gives him the old lyre so that he can continue the song of life. Here, as Hesiod and Palamas become one, the old and the new unite. The poem ends with the poetic testament of the Ascrean to Palamas:

> My simple songs, my humble words,
> found fire in Tartarus and light in the Elysian fields.
> And now they return. Hear them again: deep, epic, great,
> touched by the mystic circles of the lower world.
> My stammer has become the word; the water drop a spring.
> Here is my soul—take it in your young body and make it yours!

In "The Ascrean" the broken and desperate poet regains his lost faith. The beauty of his song, which unites him with the world, is a kind of catharsis for his tormented soul. But the synthesis of the antithetical forces inside him psychologically lasts only as long as his poetic sublimation supports him. For a poet like Palamas, who cannot live separately from his world, a lasting inner harmony cannot be achieved unless it has an objective counterpart. Palamas, like his time and ours, was unable to overcome the conflicts and negations of his life and give a dynamic and lasting solution to the problems of himself and his society.

V   *"The Chains"*

"The Chains," the second of the "Great Visions," was written in 1899, the year Palamas began *The Dodecalogue of the Gypsy.* Originally a part of the *Dodecalogue,* it can serve as an excellent introduction to it. In "The Chains" the poet of the tranquil "Ascrean" becomes a militant revolutionary. The iambic lines of memory and hymn make room here for short and vigorous trochaic verses suitable to a poem of action, a versification that is continued and strengthened in the *Dodecalogue.* The central theme of the poem is the struggle of man to rise in the world of Idea, this time the Freedom-Idea. Here, the movement of the poet is that of the individual with respect to society, the powerful social law. Through an allegorical device Palamas examines the bondage of man under the social law, a law almost as powerful as Fate. The individual's hypertrophic ego, nourished by the ideas of Nietzsche, is here seen as it rises above the masses toward the ideal of freedom. Thus the poem may be seen as a study of individualism, and its motto from Milton's *Paradise Lost* may be taken as the key to an individualistic interpretation of the poem: "The mind is its own place, and in itself can make a heaven of Hell, a Hell of Heaven" (Book I, 253—55). In connection with this Palamas writes:

In "The Chains," an example of genuine philosophical myth-making, the dependent part of the man of will gradually embraces the idea of the independent and unites rigidly with it. From the darkness behind the iron prison bars of determinism there begin to be defined, with the aid of the Miltonic idea, the vast horizons of subjective idealism.[19]

In the opening lines of the poem, "the man of will" is symbolized by a male leopard in his cage:

> The leopard stirred
> in his iron cage;
> he stirred as if he had never known
> iron bars or the slave's lot
> or the humility of prison
> or the tamer's rod
> or the reveling mob around him.

He is the chosen among the chosen of the prisoners. He thinks of himself not as a slave but as "innocent and a stranger." His prison is life; the prison of all men:

> All creation from stone to mind,
> every living thing
> every mode of art
> all lines, colors, hours, cycles,
> all seasons and all lands
> made the mighty castle.

Blackman, the prison keeper, is a symbol of the collective social law. There are chains everywhere: "the world seems bound with chains/ breathing prison air." The chains symbolize the laws and conventions of society or the individual's conscience. Strangely, a musical sound rises from the chains; they have a "living tongue" which, however, is old and cursed. But from the poet's chains comes a different music, the new consciousness. He feels something stirring in them that is going to transform the world:

> Tyrants though you are, in vain;
> something stirs inside you
> to become, little by little,
> spirit and nightingale.

Blackman notices the uniqueness of the poet-prisoner, loosens his chains, and allows him to walk about a little; the social law becomes more flexible, determinism is challenged. This increases the faith of the prisoner in the possibility of freedom. As he walks in the prison he finds three lamps representing charity, help, and love. These virtues are part of the social instinct which the poet acutely possesses and which urge him to aid his fellow prisoners:

> I have come, abandoned flock,
> like a caring shepherd to bring
> a little grass adorned with flowers
> and rich with drops of dew.

Blackman leads him to an open courtyard. There he finds a strip of land and plants wheat, a poplar tree, and a lily—symbols of charity, help, and love, respectively: "And the barren earth became a garden more beautiful than a home built for newlywed lovers." Blackman then shows the poet a strange and distant skylight. The light attracts him like a magnet, and he begins a tortuous ascent on a "monstrous ladder" toward the light:

> Broken nails, sharp stones, and pebbles
> Wore and tore my tender hands,
> and my weakened feet were bleeding.
>
> And I felt that every rung
> Wrenched from me a vital part,
> Spent my hope and faith and power;
> And I panted, suffered, trembled,
> Felt my end was drawing near,
> And I climbed still on. . . .

He finally reaches the skylight. With "thirsty eyes" he looks toward the source of light and sees:

> . . . skies without end
> seas without shores;
>
> . . . .
>
> Images of perfect thought
> beyond man's comprehension.

In this boundless world live the free men of the future. "Necessity held them no more—a divine love reigned here, unchained—and they were made of the stuff of wings." The poet forgets his chains while the vision lasts and speaks to the chained throngs below. His prophetic voice resounds from the heights of the prison, heralding the coming world of freedom for mankind: "And my words became a hymn, my chains a golden lyre." In answer to his song comes the music of the prisoners' chains; their transformation begins. And the poet concludes:

> As in all that stirs and lives
> so there is power in you,
> tyrants, chains and fates,
> that transforms you and uplifts you.
> A mysterious hand begins to bring you
> closer to the wings of birds
> and to songs of nightingales.

Poetry is again the voice of liberation. The triumphant ascent of the poet from the darkness of the prison to the light of freedom is the beginning of a movement that soon grows in complexity and intensity and culminates in *The Dodecalogue of the Gypsy*. The victory of the struggling self begins.

CHAPTER 3

The Dodecalogue of the Gypsy—*The Self Triumphs*

THE DODECALOGUE of the Gypsy (1907) is the most complete synthesis of Palamas's poetic consciousness. In the sweeping movement of this epicolyric composition the polyphonous music of the poet's soul is heard in all its tonal and thematic richness. Yet, in spite of its subjective mold, *The Dodecalogue* simultaneously reflects significant evolutionary steps in the life of Hellenism and of mankind, as well as contemporary conflicts. It is a poem of action; here the poet lives his life in the unfolding of the tale, unlike in "The Ascrean" where he reconstructs his past under the guidance of memory. And the active life of the Gypsy reflects the culmination of Palamas's own struggles.

In the illuminating Introduction to the poem Palamas writes:

I felt that I too was a Gypsy in spite of my shame to confess it; a Gypsy with all his vices and miseries. No matter how well disguised under rich garments, it was myself that I undertook to sing in the accursed race. . . . The fact that I stopped at the Gypsy shows precisely that I am a Gypsy and such is my soul. But my soul is many-sided and, though it seems to be in solitary reflection, it encloses the whole world, and its loves are innumerable. I can cry out with the poet: "A thousand fine chains of gold bind me with reality." But my greatest love is the fairy of song.

(*Works* III, 290–91)

The poem is at the same time personal and objective. The Gypsy is a symbol of the poet's life with all the sufferings and wandering of thought, as well as a symbol of humanity with its aspirations and cultural transformations. As Palamas further elucidates in the Introduction:

And then, as the thread of my song unrolled I saw that my heart is filled with mind and that its pulses are vibrating ideas; that my feelings have something musical and difficult to measure. . . . And then I saw that I am the poet—certainly a poet among many, a mere soldier of

Verse—but always the poet who strives to capture in his verses the aspirations and questions of eternal man, the anxieties and fanaticism of the citizen. It may be that I am not a good citizen but it cannot be that I am the poet of myself alone. I am the poet of my age and of my people and what I hold within me cannot be separated from the external world.

(*Works* III, 291–92)

Thus *The Dodecalogue* combines all three of Palamas's lyricisms: the individual, the national, and the universal.

Later in the Introduction the poet mentions other writers both Greek and non-Greek who wrote about Gypsies. To their realistic or Romantic types he contrasts his idealistic Gypsy and states his intention in choosing him for the poem:

The descriptive re-creation of the Gypsy life was not my intention—such a use of art does not please me. The Gypsy was only a pretext and an occasion to express, through a type fitting my soul, my intellectual conflicts.

(*Works* III, 295)

Palamas's Gypsy is a sensitive and highly civilized individual who strives to create a new world for himself and for all men.

The form of *The Dodecalogue* presents certain complications which stem mainly from the combination of several genres in a single work. Its epic, lyrical, and dramatic elements are almost equally strong. Palamas had intended to write an epic with the Gypsy as the hero, but the charge of his lyricism changed the nature of the poem. Under the lyrical requirements its mythical unity is interrupted by forward and reverse jumps in time and by changes in locale. Palamas was aware of these weaknesses in the poem and tried to explain them in terms of poetic practices:

There is no definite idea of time in the poem. It seems that not even Homer has a clear sense of the passage of time—epic writers do not trouble themselves much with such matters. . . . Thus I have my hero involved in situations and concerns which are separated by long periods of time. This is because I do not relate events quietly and regularly. Instead, I employ diverse artistic devices in order to make clearer what I first see as a dream.

(*Works* III, 294–95)

The resulting lack of unity Palamas also attributes to the nature of modern poetry:

The new poetry has above all something fragmentary in it. This is a characteristic that makes a poem differ from regularly and symmetrically constructed works with a beginning, middle, and end; that presents it like a fragment of another poem which we do not know, something without beginning and end which terminates but does not give rest—like Wagner's "interminable melody."

(*Works* III, 296)

The lack of a definite mythical and temporal order is compensated by the effect of the lyrical sweep which gives a musical unity to the poem. Thus, *The Dodecalogue* can be seen as twelve lyrical movements unified by the poet's psychological unity. It was written over a period of eight years (1899–1907). The order of the twelve songs as published is not the same as the chronological order of their birth; the arrangement took place after their composition.

About the lyrical passion of the Gypsy and the unifying power of his music Palamas writes: "My Gypsy does not offer wine; he plays the violin, pours sound" (*Works* III, 298). The musical nature of the Gypsy is felt throughout the poem which, in the words of Palamas, is "language becoming a song." And it is significant that the composer, Manos Kalomoiris, who has set parts of the poem to music, told Palamas: "When I read *The Dodecalogue of the Gypsy* I was certain that you knew music.[1] Palamas, however, never studied the "divine art," as he called it.

The twelve songs are followed by a short poem, "To a Woman," which is entirely different in form, tone, and content from the preceding twelve songs. It is significant only as a psychological note on the poet, representing an unmasking of the poet-Gypsy, a return to the tormented creator-man.

I   *"The Arrival"*

The poem begins with an epic description of the arrival of the Gypsies in Thrace, the "source of peoples and ages." It is an early morning in spring as the Gypsies move against the background of Constantinople. They come from the most remote corners of the earth, beating never-ending paths. They seem to have lost their way and with it their "will and hope and memory." Among them are musicians who sing of their "hidden sorrows with sounds that tear and wound." There are fortunetellers whose eyes pierce the dark weavings of Fate. They are all Gypsies, lashed by storms and burned by desert suns. They come like "strange black birds foretelling a wild spring." The passing of the Gypsies evokes a feeling of the restless movement of humanity in history. The allusions to dawn and spring are indications of Palamas's hopes for the cultural regeneration of his people. At the same time they anticipate the Gypsy's future actions.

At this point the Gypsy, who is the idealized type of his race, appears on the scene. In a fiery monologue he speaks of himself and his race. He is alone, free from social and family ties. In the midst of life's storms he rides unconquered on his "black stubborn mule." The mule is a uniquely gifted animal since it has assimilated the best qualities of two distinct natures. The Gypsy identifies his fate with that of the mule, which symbolically combines endurance and freedom, strength of body and of will. The mule may also be seen as a symbol of destiny itself. As the Gypsy rides his mule, so he dominates his destiny, and consequently shapes his own life. It is particularly the anger and the stubbornness of the mule that attract him. With it he can wander anywhere across the unbeaten regions of the earth. And he rides triumphantly through time and space in the journey of human life that has no end. His home is the earth and his roof the sky. The cavity of an old tree or the wall of a rock are sufficient night shelter whenever he interrupts his "racing life" for a moment. And yet, in this life of wandering and hardships, the Gypsy is able to "adorn the crown" of his thought and the "wreath of his dream." From his entire life unfolds a vision which has the colors of dawn. The Gypsy sees himself rising to become a leader:

> I was unique
> in the race of the chosen,
> closing within me all the youths
> and the old ages,
> seeds and wombs inseparable.

(Works III, 314)

"The Arrival" serves as an introduction to *The Dodecalogue.* The Gypsies appear near Constantinople at a time of spiritual crisis and decline (c. 1400). It is the time when the world of the Middle Ages is dying and the Renaissance is about to begin. In choosing this time and setting for his poem, Palamas reflects his attitudes toward the culture in which he lives. Both he and the Gypsy face a decaying world and both become prophets of a renaissance. The movement of the Gypsies unfolds like a new genesis in the chaotic darkness of the world. Symbolically, the Gypsies drag with them the long history of an old but unconquered humanity and the potential fertility of spring. The Gypsy embodies the entire past and contains the seeds of the future. His uniqueness springs from his complete freedom and his ability to create his own destiny.

II *"The Toiler"*

The Gypsy, although an independent individualist, inevitably comes in contact with the social body. And the first demand of society from the individual is that he participate in one of its functions. But before the Gypsy chooses his place within the social structure, he asks his soul to assist him in his choice; here begins the Gypsy's search for self-knowledge. His questioning voice returns from the depths of his consciousness, transformed, and tells him that in order to become a leader he must first become a common worker, "one of the innumerable supporting columns of the social edifice." The individual must first subject himself to the power of the whole. Thus the Gypsy becomes a blacksmith and, with fire and hammer, shapes many tools and instruments—mighty weapons in the hands of working humanity. He forges swords and shields for soldiers. "nails for the crucifixion of the prophet," chains with which to bind evil, and church bells that disturb "the ocean of the soul." But the finished products of his toil trouble and disappoint him:

> But in vain, in vain!
>
> Abandon the iron, my hand.
> You, hammer and anvil, stop your war.
> I am the artisan smith
> who willed to make one work
> and forged another.

(Works III, 319)

He is the magician of fire who incorporates in his creations more than society expects. Men expect from his hands something durable and practical, but instead he gives them "a little soul, a beam of light, a spray of foam." He sees that his genius extends beyond the utilitarian demands of his society and abandons his vulcanic craft. Here begins the discord between the Gypsy and his society.

As soon as he throws the hammer away, a new plan springs in his mind. He seizes the gypsy oboe, becomes a musician, and travels across many lands. He plays his oboe for the "festivals of men in caves, prisons, steppes, and palaces." Men everywhere tell him: "Musician, attune your oboe song to the rhythm of our passions" (*Works* III, 322). His music, however, gives pleasure only to others; it leaves him unsatisfied because he is performing a prescribed social function.

One day he wanders alone along the shore of a lake. The calmness of the water and the beauty of the surroundings touch his soul. This is the moment of tranquillity when the sensitive ear bends to the earth "to hear the secret of life, about to be revealed." But he is suddenly possessed by a mad desire to "abuse the sacred mystery" and in its place to awaken the "cry of the gypsy oboe." As his shrieking oboe destroys the harmony of nature, the Gypsy bends over the water and sees his disfigured and frightful face. In anger he then shatters his oboe, and so destroys one more link with society. Once more he revolts against his socially imposed function because it is not in agreement with his longings for a higher, more personal harmony. And he continues his quest for a more satisfying involvement.

He becomes a mason and "builds palaces where huts stood." With his own hands he molds all materials to forms which adorn "man's beautiful temple"—civilization. Each individual work fascinates him. But when he attempts to see a master plan of the whole in unity, he realizes his failure. In its entirety his work is strange and incomprehensible because the Gypsy does not see his soul in it. The social structure distorts the individual conception. Once more the Gypsy fails to harmonize the self with society; and once again he takes the solitary path. But his departure from work and society is not without pain. He had loved his involvement as creative action, and now that he is severed from his work, he sings a hymn of incomparable beauty. Fire and music and the builder's dream are still in his soul, for he has lived through them the unforgettable days of creative toil.

The Gypsy gradually moves toward a more personal creative life where beauty lives according to the individual's measure. But there are other experiences that must enrich his consciousness before the final stage is reached. Though disappointed and embittered, he moves on toward new paths.

III *"Love"*

Attempting to discover the source of his inspiration in the writing of *The Dodecalogue,* Palamas writes:

Who knows what gypsy woman, years ago, spoke palpitating words to my heart! And how the first quatrain sprang!—the protoplasm around which later, little by little, my creation grew:

> Partridge-breasted gypsy,
> enchantress, you who speak
> a commanding tongue
> to the midnight stars . . .

(Works III, 289-90)

These are the opening lines of the Gypsy's song of love and should be seen in relation to Palamas's ideas on creative inspiration, ideas which are basically Freudian: "And what else, in its roots, is art, the sister of love, but a deep carnal excitement which gathers many other elements and so is transformed and sublimated into a rich body with many breaths."[2] Thus from the Gypsy woman Palamas passed to the Gypsy man, then to the race, and finally to humanity.

In this song the Gypsy offers his passion and his music to the woman he loves. Through love he yearns to achieve a union of flesh and spirit, of the particular and the universal which is like the union of Logos and Rhyme for the creation of Poetry. Out of the Gypsy's union with woman, new men will spring who will be either singers or leaders. And the new life will be created by the full participation and balance of the Apollonian and the Dionysian forces of man. The last-born of the generation will be the most complete and the strongest of all men:

> And the Highest Man shall come
> whose sword even
> will shine
> like a harmonious lyre.

(Works III, 332)

This Superior Man, the creative individual, will destroy with his sword, the power of will, all the evils of society.

For the love of woman the Gypsy denies all gods and all values:

> I know nothing of religions
> and never bow to any gods.
> You are my wisdom and my faith!
> I plundered all the temples,
>
> I stripped the shrines
> and profaned the altar,
> the sacred relics, the holy Cross,
> and all the sacred offerings:

> chalices, chandeliers—
> all that the heart reveres;
> and I threw them, an armful of flowers,
> for you to trample.

(Works III, 333)

But soon he awakens to a new disillusionment. He sees that love, as actual life offers it, is neither a source of wisdom nor a begetter of ideal men. The woman does not give strength for self-protection; she gives only physical pleasure. For the creative side of the Gypsy, she is only a deceiving and blinding enchantress:

> In your full, conquering
> breasts I only found
> the woman's deception,
> and the slavery of flesh. . . .

(Works III, 333)

So dies the Gypsy's hope in love. But his experience of love, though weakening and disillusioning like the experiences of toil and creation, strengthens his will and intensifies his passion for the ideal. As soon as he negates and destroys one form of life, he begins to search for another; and each known form enables him to create a new one, more complete than the last.

IV *"The Death of the Gods"*

In this song the Gypsy declares his complete unbelief in gods and negates every known religion. At first he seems to raise his voice against them without first having experienced the life of a believer. But the Gypsy, as a sensitive man, knows and understands religions because values of a religious nature are inevitable legacies of every tradition; gods as eternal symbols permeate every sensitive individual's consciousness. The Gypsy knows all gods but remains free of their domination:

> In every land where I journeyed
> I raised my tent in front of temples;
> I have known the church, the mosque, the monastery
> and exchanged swift and sharp words
> with believers and levites.
> Basilicas have seen me in the early dawn,
> and I passed many nights in hermitages and cloisters.

> Everywhere, from the ruins of pagan Greece
> to the richly ornamented pagodas,
> I sniffed and contemptfully stripped
> all the roses of worship.
> And I stood stranger and free
> of all adorations, prayers, and vows.
> I am the prophet of the unbelievers
> and it is my life that is the miracle.

(Works III, 335)

All gods tempted the Gypsy with the promise of heavenly tranquillity. But all of them are outside the human realm, and the Gypsy abhors anything that is not human or humanly measured. He loves the earth and human life above all else. The gods are creations of man's need and fear. They are immobile and dead compared to the dynamic movement of the Gypsy-rider. As he travels, the world shifts before him and values change with space and time. When he stops things become fixed and lifelesss:

> I am the one who runs, not you.
> You are bound to the soil with your roots;
> the rider has only to stop
> and you become fixed again.

(Works III, 337)

Everything is relative and depends on the strength of man the creator.

Since there is nothing bigger than man for the Gypsy, what reigns outside man is the "great Nothing," whose prophet he becomes. His tone here is reminiscent of Zarathustra's cry: "God is dead." The Gypsy, who now represents a thorough skepticism, has destroyed the absolute values established by religion. In the temple of negation the only standing statue is the "monster Nothing." And in the absence of gods, the loneliness of the Gypsy becomes greater; he is alone now, completely alone, not only among men but in the entire universe. Yet his passion for self-integration leads him on to new and greater experiences.

V *"The Death of the Ancients"*

The Gypsy continues to attack and destroy the sterile and lifeless values of society. He now turns his rage on the remnants of the ancient world which live in the lethargic minds of some Classicists. The song begins with the description of a dramatic moment in the history of

Hellenism. It is the time of the fall of Constantinople, the end of a long and magnificently blended tradition. The spiritual leaders of Hellenism are about to flee to the West. The precious relics of thought and worship are reverently placed aboard strange ships to be transplanted to the sleeping West and kindle its renaissance. Books, chalices, and statues are carried by the fleeing sages who believe that the ancient ideas will rise again like suns:

> We will spread like a spring of mind
> and in barren lands and old ages
> we will sow Greece and youth.
>
> . . . .
>
> Monks and pontifices
> shall fall at Helen's feet
> and shall worship the swan of Eurotas.
>
> (*Works* III, 349—'50)

This is what the traditionalists believe, and consequently they attempt to incorporate the Classical forms of life, unchanged, into the modern world. But the Gypsy knows that it is impossible to create a sound civilization through the adoption of old values:

> Another air for you now
> and another sun;
> you will never live a full life again
> O beautiful phantoms.
>
> (*Works* III, 352)

Only that which breathes in the living people of each age can create a civilization in harmony with the laws of change. Many men and cultures will adopt the Classical values, but "there is only one Greece and she is gone forever/ gone—and weep for her!"

Every age that will attempt to build a culture completely based on old patterns inevitably will die forgotten. It is right to search for inspiration and wisdom in the past, but only those who are free of its complete domination can create a significant civilization. "Progress for the free, for us!" the Gypsy cries. Yet he calls the ancients his brothers because they pass like the Gypsies, free and unconquered, sowing the seed of freedom where slavery reigns.

> . . . white, luminous brothers
> of our black race,
> you, like our tribe, will never anchor
> anywhere!

(Works III, 353)

This is how the Gypsy speaks to the procession of sages and saints who are moving toward the ships of exile as the destroyer Sultan rides into the ruined City.

With the death of the ancients, another set of "eternal" values crumbles. The Gypsy now possesses greater freedom and strength. His individualism becomes supreme as he stands above his race at the end of history destroying the past, reconstructing the present, and planning the future. Palamas, likewise, stands as a critic and cultural leader of his people.

VI *"Around the Fire"*

The Gypsy now encounters, face to face, the Christians and the pagans of his time. One morning as he wanders on the barren land outside Constantinople he sees a fire and a crowd of people around it. They are Christians burning heretic books.[3] The Gypsy discerns in their movements a rhythm which springs from "fear and delight." In the flames the books look "like hands, faces, and bodies" out of which spirits rise and "join the singing larks." A little further the Gypsy sees a group of pagans and philosophers, "the hunters of dreams." The Christians, in a hymn of their auto-da-fe, blame the pagans for the evils of society and burn every book that is inspired by "Satan's breath." Then follows a hymn of the pagans praising the ancient spirit of order and beauty, the world that is now dying under the black cloak of the monk. The Gypsy listens to the Christians and the pagans and then attacks both, for their spirits live like "monsters in the depths of the ocean," never seeing the sun. To him they are all idol worshipers because they do not take their light from the living sun. The Olympian minds and the crosses of Golgotha, the virgin Athena and the Virgin Mary, have no creative power for the building of a new world.

The struggle of the Christians to bring back their original mystical faith is in vain because the "golden-winged eagle of thought" is a growing reality. The pagan struggle to destroy Christianity is also in vain since "it was not for nothing that the Nazarene was crucified."

The Gypsy believes that there are similarities between the pagans and the Christians: "The Crucifixes shine like Apollo/ and every Christ holds an Orphean lyre" (*Works* III, 363). He thinks that some day they will unite in the enjoyment of a new life "saturated with the saps of spring." The "new men" are the healthy people of the mountains who have not known books and sacraments; yet they know instinctively the old values which they blend and transform:

> The milk of health and the blood of sacrifice
> are mingled in them;
> and under their forested chests
> a vast heart proclaims—
> through sacrifice, battle and song—
> the new life and truth.

(*Works* III, 365)

In his negation of traditional forms of life, Palamas is not inspired by philosophical and historical studies as much as he is by direct contact with his people. He sees around him fanatic theologians and empty scholars living with ideas that are incapable of solving the problems of the time. He uses historical situations to show more dramatically the antinomies existing between Christianity and paganism. And the hymns of the two camps express the two world views that shaped modern Greece and the Western world. Palamas certainly carries in himself the same conflicting elements and so, here again, he expresses both an historical and a personal reality. And in the relationship of Classicism and Christianity, as Palamas presents it, lies the basic foundation of the Greek historical character:

Palamas believes that in the antagonism of the pagan and the Christian elements of the Greek consciousness lies the cornerstone of our entire psychology and history. . . . He . . . formulated and made conscious the tragic beauty of our historical destiny and he succeeded in this because his own personality contained the same destiny and beauty.[4]

This struggle of Classicism and Christianity is a central theme in the cultural history of Europe. And Palamas, by continuing Goethe's synthesis of cultures and Nietzsche's re-examining of values, links himself with the core of the European tradition.

VII *"The Festival at Kakava"*

On the first day of May the Gypsies begin to celebrate their only holiday. From all parts of the world they gather at Kakava, near the walls of Constantinople, for their festivities and tribal ceremonies. This festival symbolically captures the richness and vitality of human life in all its colors and rhythms. The Gypsies with their many skills and diverse functions represent every characteristic and potentiality of man. Their movement in this song is similar to that in "The Arrival," only here it is richer and more complex. Now, they are not simply traveling but gathering for a purpose: their greatest feast, the orgy of spring.

Many of them started from the land of the Ganges, the birthplace of their race. They passed through Egypt where the Sphinx was astonished seeing in them "something more enigmatic than her own face." They are now in Constantinople where their dynamism and creativity are contrasted to the dying Byzantine culture. Byzantium has lived for centuries under an unchanged order where nothing new and regenerating could enter. It is an example of a culture with absolute values which decays because of the rigidity and anachronism of those values. The Gypsies, on the contrary, constantly change occupations, climate, and language. They symbolize an ever-regenerating and ever-transforming culture, admitting in itself new values which perpetuate its life. The Gypsies are unconquerable, prepared to meet "all fates and all weathers."

On the third day of the fair when the festivities are at their climax, a messenger of the Emperor addresses the Gypsies. He announces that the Emperor is offering them land on which to make their home. This would require the Gypsies to become citizens of a nation and defenders of its territory. Before the messenger can finish his speech, however, the Gypsy, "the one who lives for a thousand," rises to speak to his people. With the prophetic voice of a seer he urges them not to accept such a binding offer because the Gypsies are made to live free, to wander over the vast earth. The cities, he tells them, are "dens of the vile people and shelters of the weak." For the Gypsies the world is one, and if they must have a homeland, "it shall extend as far as the kingdom of the sun." They must not take root in one place and live under the laws of one state; their only law is freedom and no force can supersede it. Even if their first fatherland were offered to them, they should refuse it for the reality of the present:

> ... No. It is not for us.
> Do not spoil our feast.
> We celebrate the smashing of chains,
> be they of diamond or of steel.
> We are the mighty liberated of the earth.
> To hell with all fatherlands!

(Works III, 383)

The Gypsies will destroy all fatherlands, and mankind will then live in joy:

> We are the race Fate has chosen
> to strike the deathblow on fatherlands.
>
> . . . .
>
> All nations forming one gypsy world,
> gloriously enthroned, creating
> with hammer and violin
> man's highest Ideal. All creation
> is a festival in a garden of May
> and all the Earth a fatherland.

> (Works III, 383—'84)

The Gypsy sees political and moral corruption within the boundaries of the state and inside the city walls. Underneath the shield of national structure operate disintegrating forces. Grouping under a national ideal results in a narrowing of man's view of humanity. Also, a narrow social confinement creates a rigidity of values and ideas which opposes the movement of man toward progress and freedom.

"The Fair at Kakava" is also a symbolic picture of a form of skepticism which is found in Palamas and his world. The phases and movements of the Gypsy life are like the numerous oscillations of skeptical thought. The skeptic constantly entertains new and old ideas but never arrives at a final acceptance of one form. Like the Gypsies, the skeptic wanders in the world of relative values and negates all absolutes.

For Palamas, "fatherland" symbolizes the entire cultural body of a nation and particularly the institutional forms which, during the last half of the nineteenth century, were but a heap of ancient "glories" and ideas unable to contain the anxieties of modern man. With the denouncement of fatherlands, Palamas reaches the highest point in his revolt against tradition and the lowest point on the ladder of negation.

VIII *"The Prophet"*

This song presents some problems of interpretation which arise from its independent standing—independent in terms of the central mythical unfolding of the poem. For the first time the Gypsy is not present; a mysterious prophet takes his place. The content has no direct bearing on the Gypsy or his people, but refers exclusively to Greek history. If the Gypsy is identified with the prophet, as some critics have suggested, the interpretation is narrowed to a national setting. A psychological approach and an allegorical treatment of the prophet's speech, however, lead to a more encompassing and more satisfactory interpretation.

The prophet, who like Zarathustra left the wilderness, appears in Constantinople before its fall. In the Hippodrome the decadent Emperor and his nobles are playing their evil games while the shadow of destruction spreads over the empire. The valiant *akrites,* the defenders of the frontier, try in vain to awaken the celebrating populace. It is at this moment that the voice of the prophet, a voice of biblical grandeur, is heard foretelling the destruction of the sinful City.

Through the words of the prophet Palamas portrays the death of an old world. All the values that the Gypsy negated are actually destroyed in the collapse of the Byzantine state, which stands for any decaying culture. But Palamas is not solely concerned with the death of a culture. Above all, he expresses himself, the despair of the Gypsy-poet, who, having destroyed all values, comes to the point of self-destruction, since his life has no meaning in a cultural vacuum. Palamas, like Nietzsche, believed that in order to understand oneself and to become a superior individual, one must first "die"—descend into Avernus. And the Gypsy's death is presented allegorically and paradoxically by the death of the very values he negated. The sinful soul of the city, whose death the prophet foretells, is also the soul of the Gypsy. Palamas shows here the unbreakable unity between the individual and society, between himself and the fate of Hellenism in particular.

In "The Prophet" Palamas's "kassianism" finds its boldest expression. Here we find the mystical experience which enabled the Gypsy to ascend from the depths of remorse and destruction to the summit of positive creation. The last verses of "The Prophet" describe this magnificent ascent:

> And you will hear the redeemer's voice,
> You will strip off the garments of sin,
> and, finding again your strength and freedom,
> you will stir like grass and like a bird,
> like a woman's breast and a wave.
> And having reached the lowest rung
> on the ladder of Evil,
> you will feel wings growing on you—O joy!
> for the heights that invite you,
> your great wings of times past!

> (*Works* III, 400)

Life begins again at the lowest depths of degradation, or, to borrow an existentialist phrase, at the "far side of despair." The savior for the dying state will be the historical law that governs the decline and rise of nations. For the Gypsy-poet, as the next song will show, the savior is art. But the Gypsy-poet realizes that his old self can no longer satisfy him. As society must reconstruct itself in order to rise again, so he must re-create himself.

In "The Prophet" Palamas's three lyricisms are intensely concentrated and heightened. The lyricism of "we" appears in the background as the historical fate of Hellenism, the lyricism of "I" in the "kassianic" soul of which the poet sings, and the lyricism of "all" in the timeless wisdom of the prophet.

IX   *"The Violin"*

In "The Violin" the regeneration of the Gypsy-poet begins to take shape. At the opening of the song the Gypsy-poet is in a twilight state between despair and awakening; he sees death and life mingled in himself:

> If I am like a tree
> and in my branches sing
> a thousand multicolored birds—
> a thousand songs in my foliage—
> my trunk is hollow
> and in it toads, insects, reptiles
> have set up their dwellings.
> On my topmost branches rests shiny dew
> but in my roots, poison.
>
> . . . .
>
> I have the sun on my face
> but in my heart's depths hell lives.

(Works III, 402)

One day, as he wanders in despair, the Gypsy finds an old violin which once belonged to the "Old Man," a sage who lived in caves with wild beasts and spirits. The Gypsy takes the violin in his hands and begins to play. The music gives him joy and inspiration; art regenerates and heightens life. The Gypsy is aware of the great artistic tradition the "Old Man" represents and believes that his mission is to continue it.

> Strike my bow and build;
> the world is created
> by the action of my hands.
>
> . . . .
>
> My violin, only you exist,
> And there is only one language, your sound,
> one creator and he is I,
> and one miracle-working word—
> the logos that is music.
>
> (*Works* III, 405)

Plato's maxim. "Music make and create," the motto of *The Dodeca-logue,* is here realized. The poet's music-making action is raised to a religious level; art reveals the essence of life. Logos, like poetry, is the product of the union of music and meaning. This union is achieved after a long struggle of the artist:

> . . . the great world
> is always created from a struggle
> like that of the bow with the strings.
> And what is beautiful and noble on earth
> is always born in the rage of battle,
> fathered by the victor.
>
> (*Works* III, 406)

The strengthening of music comes to the Gypsy when he is in the middle of his journey and at a moment of psychological paralysis and rational weakness. Now he turns to the people and plays his new song for them. But they are disturbed and unable to understand his transformation. His present ideas are as revolutionary as those of his destructive period. Only the children, who represent the future, love his song, and the Gypsy turns to them. The children will be immersed in his music from the beginning and will thus be able to understand it and build the world that his song inspires.

X *"Resurrection"*

In this song the Gypsy, with the help of his violin, brings back to life "love," "fatherland," and "gods." Gypsy and violin are here united as one force. Palamas, like Nietzsche and Wagner, believed in the regenerating power of music, and his Gypsy, like a mythical Dionysos, undertakes the regeneration of the world through the power of poetry:

The immortals who died
and whom I buried with my hands,
the immortals who are dead
you shall bring to life,
O music of resurrection!

(Works III, 412)

The Gypsy goes to a cemetery where three tombs of "marble and gold" stand distinct from the others. They enclose "love," "fatherland," and "gods." The magic music of the Gypsy moves the tombstones and brings all three back to life. "Fatherland" returns as an ideal environment, a state governed by wise men and inhabited by free citizens. The "gods" come to life as symbols of what is beautiful and true, and they are "enthroned on the highest summit of the Idea." "Love" also returns to life as an ideal. She is again the "enchantress who speaks a commanding language," but now as a purely creative force bearing the "perfect children" of the Idea.

Through this resurrection the Gypsy brings into being new values for himself and for society. The most important quality of these values is that they are *resurrected:* they embody the wisdom of tradition, the purging of death, and the vigor of new life. Their ideal nature is not an indication of an unchanging character, but of recurrence and changeability. Their final form and interstructure depend on the particular demands of time and milieu. The new values have a historical content which necessitates their change as types. But they also have a suprahistorical character which, as idea, never changes.

XI *"The Legend of Adakrytos"*

In the next song the Gypsy as the Superior Man appears full grown, though in the context of an allegory. An old Oriental tale provides the background for the legend of Adakrytos, the man who never weeps. The Gypsy identifies himself with Adakrytos and tells the story of his life. Adakrytos is the only son of rich and loving parents, who sacrifice their entire fortune for his joys and education. But Adakrytos, never satisfied with all that their sacrifices obtain for him, sells them as slaves. With the price of his mother he buys golden garments and with that of his father a riding horse. Hearing of this cruel act, the king of the land orders Adakrytos into exile to the kingdom of his brother, to whom Adakrytos is to deliver a sealed message. During the long journey to his exile, Adakrytos is lost in the dessert and is tortured by great thirst. As he later uses the message scroll to drink water with, he discovers that it contains his death sentence, which is to be carried out by the king to whom he is going. To save his life he goes to another land. Here lives the beautiful and wise princess Aghelasti, the one who never laughs. Her father has proclaimed that Aghelasti will marry the man whose questions she is unable to answer. Many wise princes found death with the answer of heartless Aghelasti. Adakrytos asks her to solve the following riddle, which is the riddle of his own life:

> "Riding on my father,
> I wore my mother;
> and to quench my thirst
> I drank water with my death."

(Works III, 434)

Aghelasti cannot answer and Adakrytos takes her as his wife. Then he returns to his homeland, kills the king, but refuses the throne offered to him by the people. The legend ends with Adakrytos's vision of the future, the life of his progeny.

Adakrytos is the Gypsy-Superior Man who in his youth spent and abused the legacies of his tradition. He even sold his parents, his fatherland, and gods. The king who ordered him into exile represents society. Adakrytos cannot be destroyed by his own society and is sent to another. His wanderings in the desert stand for the loneliness and endurance through which the Superior Man must be tested. His thirst represents his longing for knowledge. The horse symbolizes the power of reason. It was his horse that saved him from death and led him to Aghelasti, who symbolizes science and uncompromising reason. Her rigidity and wisdom are ideal qualities as a mate to the Superior Man; the riddle and each detail of the legend stand for various aspects of his character and his life.

After his rejection of the throne, which shows his rejection of the established order, Adakrytos plans to create with Aghelasti the race of Superior Men. He leaves his people again in order to live in the wilderness. A joyful hymn now rises from his soul as his "time-piercing glance" reads the future:

> In the cycles of the Ages all things
> go, return, change—remain the same.
> And a day will come,
> when all creation shall tremble;
> but you my children will stand,
> firm columns supporting the world.

(Works III, 436)

So the Gypsy now completes the cycle of his life as action: destruction, resurrection, and creation. His psychological movement is relatively simple, while his ideological wanderings reflect the skepticism and the complexity of his age. A final triumph on the wings of poetry will close his life cycle.

XII   *"The World"*

In the last of the twelve songs the Gypsy returns to nature from which he emerged; he actually comes back to the forests of Thrace where he first appeared. He speaks to the trees and asks them to accept him in their world:

> Injured by man
> I come to you, pure forests.
> Embrace me and hear me;
> my violin is a soul.
>
>   *(Works* III, 438)

Upon seeing the Gypsy-musician, the trees are reminded of Orpheus who went to nature a broken man but soon rose to create a second Olympus. They begin to sing a hymn of life which reveals to him the "fate and history of the Earth." The Gypsy learns that truth is found in the complete unity of man and nature. He is told to make his violin resonate the harmony of truth and to create a third Olympus with the power of science. Each Olympus is a peak, a great moment of development in the history of humanity. The first Olympus, the pantheistic, was characterized by the dominance of physical forces, the second by the spiritual and mystical power of music which created it. The third, the Gypsy's creation, will be based on the knowledge of the laws of nature and on art.

Palamas does not explain here exactly what this new queen, science, whom the Gypsy enthrones on the third Olympus, is. Her nature must be surmised from the entire work of Palamas. Without doubt, he does not attribute a purely rational character to science. She is the apex of a synthetic method in the search for truth, a method aided as much by music and intuition as by reason. The strong influence of the towering scientific figures of the nineteenth century on Palamas led him to an exaggeration and a hasty crowning of science, a common fault or virtue of his time. In the later years of his life Palamas grew skeptical about this queen whom he had praised in many of his works. Angelos Sikelianos quotes him uttering at a moment of meditation shortly before his death: "Science—the instrument for a possible higher civilization. Nothing more"[5]

The Gypsy's return to his point of origin takes the form of a musical and mystical attempt to unite with nature, the immutable background of objective reality. With the help of art he succeeds; he is able to unite with the entire universe. His creation of the third Olympus is, in this context, a religious activity aiming toward a cosmological unity. His relation to Orpheus shows the strong participation of the musical force in the synthetic entity which Palamas calls science. Thus, aside from the philosophical aspect of this song, there is the poetic realm in which the Gypsy becomes a purely musical being and blends triumphantly with nature. The establishment of the third Olympus, on the other hand, expresses the demand of the European mind in the last half of the nineteenth century for a positive religion based on science.

XIII *Some Critical Interpretations*

The Dodecalogue has attracted more critical attention than any other work of Palamas. There have been many and diverse interpretations of it. Seeing the work from the particular standpoint of his generation and his intellectual background, each critic singled out and stressed a particular dimension of the poem. It is natural that at the time of its appearance the critics should center their attention on the national elements and consider them primary. Thus one critic wrote in 1907 that *The Dodecalogue* is the "lawgiving dodecalogue of modern Hellenism." [6] It is, according to him, the consciousness of new Greece which has achieved its literary formulation before its national and social ones. This interpretation, although fundamentally sound, is very narrow, however, and does not follow from the personality of the Gypsy, who is the heart of the work.

As time went on, increasing emphasis was placed on the philosophical, moral, social, and esthetic elements of *The Dodecalogue*. For example, the Gypsy has been interpreted as a symbol of "free thought,"[7] or of "the evolution and end of man as Idea."[8] The social and moral interpretations of the poem, however, are predominant and seem to be increasing. Thus the Gypsy is seen by most critics as a Superior Man who is victorious in the struggle of man against time and the destructiveness of life: "The inspired Gypsy presents dynamically those moments in the life of humanity when each uniquely great individual destroys the traditional idols and then, when he finds himself in front of chaos, rebuilds them on his own foundations."[9]

The Dodecalogue, examined in relation to its contemporary milieu, is a study on the evolution of a highly individualistic personality who belongs to the romantic tradition. *"The Dodecalogue of the Gypsy* is the triumph and the shining crown of *individualism,* individualism in the broader sense of the word, which played a primary role in the development of modern civilization."[10] Ibsen's Brand and Nietzsche's Zarathustra are, in the moral sphere, the greatest heroes of this tradition, and the Gypsy of Palamas may be considered their younger brother. It must be emphasized, however, that Palamas found the inspiration and the essential materials for his creation in the conditions of his society and in his inner life. The earlier types of Ibsen and Nietzsche were secondary influences which contributed more to the development of his ideas than to his conception of them.

Palamas's Gypsy has many characteristics of the Romantic hero— passionate nature, love of freedom, and excessive individualism. But the Romantic fatalism and sense of final destruction are substituted in the Gypsy by his faith in a final unity with nature and society. The Gypsy as an individual always moves in relation to an objective background of nature or society. The subject constantly strives to relate himself with the objective world, and self-knowledge springs from his conflicts with society. Through a process of destructive and creative action, the Gypsy evolves from the free self that he was in "The Arrival" to the free social superman of the last three songs; from an individual instinctively aware of his race to a fully conscious and purposeful social being in complete communion with all humanity.

In *The Dodecalogue* Palamas does not rise to the harmony of the ideal esthetic spheres that he sought in *Life Immovable.* Here he lives in the concrete world of human situations, and his verse is constantly charged with the emotions of human involvement on the level of moral and social action. And it is in the unity of self and society that the poet achieves self-realization.

The development of the Gypsy through the necessary steps of destruction and creation of values includes many substreams of emotional and ideological significance. The Gypsy is deeply aware of his position in society and history, and he feels the entire past weighing upon him as he undertakes to create the future. This awareness turns into a "critique of cultures,"[11] past and present, some of which he completely negates in order to re-create their values according to the needs of the modern world. Art and science will guide the building of the new world. By creating the symbolic marriage of Adakrytos and

Aghelasti—art and science—he criticizes, but also partially accepts, the dominant ideological trend of his time: positivism. He remains consistent in his skepticism, a creative skepticism which leads the poet to continuously reconstruct the diverse elements of life. This is the skepticism which multiplies the forms of life and creates a protean art.

Palamas re-creates life in *The Dodecalogue* as he experienced it psychologically under the impact of historical and social forces. This life unfolds in the poem through lyrical explosions forming dialectical syntheses of self and society, present and past, death and creation, art and science. The poet's self always remains in the foreground, and through it life is presented in the dynamic forms of change and unity.

The rhythm an tone of the poem spring spontaneously from the movement of the Gypsy and remain unchanged throughout the poem. Palamas has created here a new versification, specifically for the ear, which expresses the musical nature of the Gypsy. It is an unrestrained free verse which pours itself into trochaic or iambic patterns that constantly break in lines of varying lengths, creating thus a swift and dynamic rhythm. Palamas never again employed this type of verse; it belongs exclusively to the Gypsy's personality.

All the essential ideas of Palamas are present in *The Dodecalogue*. His love of country, his Classicism, his science ideal, his poetic ideal, and his pantheism find their climactic formulation in this poem of Heraclitean movement and complexity. Palamas has drawn from many sources; folklore, memories of childhood, philosophical and literary works, science, and history, all contributed to its composition. *The Dodecalogue* is the triumph of the poet and, above all, a symbol of life in all its vitality and richness.

CHAPTER 4

On the Epic Peaks—The Self Merges with Hellenism

THE MOST SIGNIFICANT decade in Palamas's creative life closed with the publication of *The King's Flute* (1910), a long epico-lyric poem comparable, both in magnitude and in scope, to *The Dodecalogue of the Gypsy*. Taken together, the two poems present, in the widest terms, a position of the individual in the universe and a place of Hellenism in history; they reveal the poet's most complete vision of life centering on his perennial concern: Man-Hellenism.

Although certain sections of *The King's Flute* were written contemporaneously with, one even before, *The Dodecalogue,* the completed work is a descendant of *The Dodecalogue* and a complement to it. As Palamas states: *"The Dodecalogue of the Gypsy* is the gateway, the Propylaea, through which we enter into *The King's Flute*."[1] In the context of the poet's development this statement must mean that, after the subjective, highly individualized Gypsy-poet, we are confronted with an objectified hero who becomes completely identified with the destiny of Hellenism and of humanity. And the latter is, so far as Palamas's values are concerned, a more mature hero, representing a higher stage of the poet's evolution. The shift from the individual to the collective hero could have taken place only after the struggles and triumph of the Gypsy-poet.

For the creation of the Gypsy, the idealized individual, a decadent world was suitable background, and Palamas depicted crumbling Byzantium for the poem's setting. But in writing *The King's Flute,* in which the national and human fate and ideals are examined, a glorious, triumphant moment in the history of Hellenism was more fitting for his purposes. Thus, he chooses eleventh-century Byzantium and Emperor Basil II, the Bulgar-Slayer, as his hero. Now that his concerns are more strictly social and national, an evocation of the glorious past would be a positive source of inspiration, a motive for action, to the defeated, post-1897 Greeks.

Another interesting contrast in the two poems is their utterly different prosodic structure. The songs of the individualized, the singular Gypsy were cast in the unique free verse of the *Dodecalogue.* In *The King's Flute,* the traditional, national epic material was cast almost exclusively in the most traditional Greek line, the fifteen-syllable political verse—traditional but with a new vigor and brilliance characteristic of the language-maker Palamas.

Beyond the social and ideological concerns and considerations that led Palamas to shape his hero after a Byzantine prototype there were others, more clearly of an esthetic nature. The last two decades of the nineteenth century saw the publication, both inside and outside Greece, of important treatises on Byzantine life and especially of numerous Byzantine texts. Palamas and his contemporaries found in this wealth of material—folklore, language, history—a new source of inspiration that deepened their sense of tradition, of the continuity of the Greek spirit. In this climate of Byzantine rebirth the demotic tradition was extended toward the roots, and the medieval Greek past rose as a living link between the ancient past and the present. This awareness of cultural continuity inspires the imaginative unfolding of *The King's Flute.* In *The King's Flute* poetic imagination resurrects Byzantium and the Byzantine spirit in turn, inspires and vitalizes the present.

The King's Flute is divided, like the *The Dodecalogue,* into twelve songs. But in addition it contains two short introductory poems, "Prologue" and "The Widow's Son." These two poems, among the most moving passages in the work, are at first glance external, unrelated to the central myth. They illuminate, however, the poet's psychology at the time of the composition and his intentions in writing the epic.

> Dead the life-giving fires of the land.
> In church, the smithy, at home, the shop—everywhere,
> in the castle and inside the heart
> burnt-out pieces, ashes.

(Works V, 11)

These are the opening lines of the "Prologue." They speak of the general paralysis of the will, the desolation of the land after the defeat of 1897. (The "Prologue" was written in 1902.) Greece lies prostrate; there is no will for action, no hope for regeneration. And the poet feels this ruin, this misery, and laments for the lot of his people.

But suddenly out of this sense of loss rises the poet's voice: "Song of the heroes! Forward, song of the heroes!" It is a call to action, addressed first to himself. The poet's mission is to inspire and to lead his people out of the deadly slumber of defeat. The poem becomes an invocation to the heroic Muse, the only spark hidden in the ashes, to help him raise the heroic song, to nurture the hope for national regeneration. And the poet believes passionately in this regeneration:

> And when around you the creative fires light up again,
> become alive, too, o flame, and leap foward
> and sweep across the land
> and the depths of the soul-shaping and living all.
>
> . . . .
>
> and make brothers out of dreams and deeds. Forward, song!
>
> (*Works* V, 12)

But poetry—the word—must first become deed, heroic action. And the heroic past is brought forward to aid in this ritual.

In "The Widow's Son" (1886, 1906) the poet introduces his hero indirectly by first showing his roots, his ancestors. It is a dark moment in the history of Byzantium. Kroumos, the Bulgarian King, victorious over the Byzantines in the year 813, had dragged thousands of them into slavery and exile. Now, twenty years later, Kroutagos, "Bulgaria's Tzar," grants freedom to the enslaved Byzantines. In a long, magnificent passage Palamas depicts with minute detail the shame and wretchedness of the subjugated population, reflecting at the same time the lot of contemporary Greeks, those humiliated by defeat and those still unredeemed under the Turkish yoke and the Bulgarian threat.

> Slowly they pass, in flocks; the slaves, the exiles
> awkwardly move on. And from above, the throned Tzar watches.
> Women with their little ones, old men with sticks
> and you young men, your well-built structures
> bent under your heavy burdens.
> Hunger passes, misery, shame, deep fear.
>
> . . . .
>
> The enslaver always takes the roses for himself
> always leaving the sticky thistle thorns for slaves
>
> . . . .
>
> And they edge on in front of their master,
> sometimes groaning sometimes attempting to smile
> mingling in their hearts the pain of slavery with the hope of freedom.

. . . .

In front of him they pass and fall to their knees.
Only one of them refuses to bend his knees, refuses to bow.

. . . .

Look at him! Tall, unbending, handsome, noble.

. . . .

You look at him and know he has not known
the bending of the slave-toiler which his people know.

. . . .

For him the others labored in the scorching sun
for him they dressed in rags, to have him
always clothed in brilliant garb as if they expected him
to slide back the stone—to bring the resurrection.

                                                              (*Works* V, 16)

The King is astounded. "Who is he who does not bow to me?" he
asks. "He is the widow's son, the single, unique branch." The King
commands that the widow's son be brought before him. And his people
shudder. They are terrified that the King will keep him in slavery, and
how will they go on without him who is their strength and their hope.
In their desperation they turn their eyes to the King, silently begging
him to spare their beloved:

"We can't bear to be free with him far off, a slave.
Better to have irons eating out lives forever."
And the winged speech caught on and spread wide.
Like the north wind that piles wave on wave:
"We don't want to be free without him; better slaves together!"

                                                              (*Works* V, 17)

An epic digression follows here. A moment of the past, the infancy
of the widow's son, is dramatized with exquisite color. It is a hot
summer day. The slaves are reaping in the fields of exile; the widow,
once a noblewoman, is now one of the toilers. Her infant son is sleeping
in the shade of a laurel, "near the laurel's root." Suddenly, as the sun
soars into the sky, a mysterious cloud spreads over them and closes in
toward the sleeping boy. His mother shrieks in terror. The cloud

becomes an eagle soaring above her child. An old toiler who knew magic and the mantic arts looks on and speaks:

> "Great is God's mercy and glory to his mane.
> The cross-winged eagle is sent by his will.
> The stork tells when spring is coming,
> you, autumn, tell us the cyclamen is here,
> and the far-visioned eagle speaks of mighty fate.
> Where the owl is heard misfortune strikes,
> where a swallow stops happiness spreads,
> and whoever is shadowed by a cross-winged eagle
> will become a king."
>
> (*Works* V, 19)

The people rejoice:

> A cooling dew fell on the pain-withered hearts—
> let the noon harvest sun scorch on—
> and a prophetic dawn spread her soothing
> light in the joyless mind of the slave world.
> The long-winged bird winged on and vanished
> but the magic of his shadow stayed on forever.
> From that moment and that day
> the youth was their icon, icon for worship.
>
> (*Works* V, 20)

Greece, the wounded, widowed mother, looked then, as at the time of the poem's composition, for a hero-son to uplift her, to save her.

The digression ends and the poet returns to the confrontation of King and the widow's son. The King questions the proud youth, admiring his bearing and his brave, dignified answers. He offers to make him a page in his palace, but the widow's son refuses. The King's mood darkens, and his minions are furious at the youth. But the youth had answered "Kroutagos the Tzar" with such words, brave yet "sweet—modest like a girl's" and "his face shone with rose-brightness" that, despite the minions's advice to put the youth to death:

> You Kroutagos, spring up from your throne, and, upright
> you kiss the youth on the forehead and speak as a true man;
> "Go back to your mother and to your people run;
> revel in your youth, enjoy your fearless pride,
> and if you are a lion's son, I am the lion! . . ."
>
> (*Works* V, 21)

The poem ends with a description of the people's joy, in a

magnificent simile reminiscent of Homer, and the voice of a prophetic bird, straight out of the demotic tradition, which foretells of the glory of Byzantium under the rulers of the Macedonian dynasty that was founded by the "Widow's son."

With the two introductory poems Palamas has brilliantly linked the present with the past and has magically created the atmosphere in which his hero is about to breathe.

I *First Song*

In the second edition of *The King's Flute* (1920), Palamas included short interpretive plot summaries, one for each song, in order to aid the reader in his understanding and appreciation of the poem. These synopses will be used here, each introducing a song, in order to facilitate the analysis and achieve greater brevity.

It is the time when Emperor Michael Paleologos was besieging Frankish-occupied Constantinople. Officers of the Byzantine army are reveling in an abandoned monastery outside the City. There they see an open grave and, leaning against it, a human skeleton with a reed flute in its mouth—as it has been told by the Byzantine chroniclers. From the epigraph of the tomb they surmise that the skeleton with the flute is that of the Emperor Basil the Bulgar-Slayer, who died one hundred years earlier. Astonishment. They worship the remnants. They send a messenger to Paleologos. They want to take the flute out of the mouth of the skeleton—most likely put there as a joke. The jeering flute becomes a symbolic, mysterious, epic flute. It speaks, sings, chants— keeps the revelers spell bound. From this point the poem becomes one with the flute's song—at once epic, lyrical, historical, philosophical, mystical, prophetic; the poet's breath and the king's soul are indissolubly bound together in an atmosphere of a visionary dream, where real and transcendental elements co-exist.

Palamas bases the main thrust of the plot in this song on two incidents from the life of his hero which are described by contemporary historians. The first has to do with the hero's grave and the flute found in his skeleton's mouth. This offers unlimited possibilities to the poet, and he exploits them fully. The second incident deals with the historically verified pilgrimage of the hero to Athens where he prayed and offered gifts to the Virgin Mary, worshiped in the Christianized temple of the Parthenon. There is history here, at the base, but it is often transformed to myth. And the poetic imagination carries out the transformation.

"The City, see it there! Out there on the epic Plain." This is the opening line of the first song. Constantinople is the focal point. She is occupied by the Frankish Crusaders. The Byzantine army under the command of Michael Paleologos is planning an attack to liberate her. She is a captive, the area all around her desolate—"barren the epic Plain." The monastery where the officers are reveling is in ruins.

It is against this background that the remains of the glorious emperor are found. His skeleton alone is enough to send shivers across the camp.

> Nothing of him remained; only a flute
> in the hole that was once the mouth.
> You would think he stood upright, longing to open
> the gates to the other world, for the strangest vision. . .
>
> (*Works* V, 29)

And the dead king magically comes to life. Before the reviling flute can be touched, it comes alive, becomes an endless song:

> I am the epic flute, the prophetic reed;
> Kleio's twin sister I am, the tongue of Kalliope.
> Sibyl's glance gave me the dark-piercing vision
> and in my entrails Kassandra's shriek still echoes.
>
> . . . .
>
> My birthgivers are the mystical the terrible Mothers.[2]
> My tongue and visage a flute, though I take
> a thousand forms. My song is prophecy and my music law.
> With wings of dream I fly, free of all support,
> passing through ages and over lands
> and you transport me my ship, sea demon, Imagination.
>
> (*Works* V, 32)

The poet turns the flute "into an instrument of prophecy and a judge of history."[3] This is the supreme function of poetry. As Palamas has written in his *Poetics:* "If we must stamp the poet's brow with a word that could evoke the true meaning of his mission, no word would be more fitting than the word prophet."[4]

The First Song is another step in the poet's elaborate process of introducing the reader to the heroic world. The hero has not been directly introduced, but the step is immense. Magic and legend have worked their miracles.

II *Second Song*

Episodic. On the Prinkipo Islands. A picture of the natural landscape
and a resurrection of the historical reality; the shades—always living—of
emperors and empresses that embraced the monastic life there, exiled,
fallen, wretched. Romanos Diogenes, Rangavés, Lekapenós, Eiréne the
Athenian, appear, quickly sketched in their historical context. Above
all the two great warriors, after the hedonist Romanos: Nikephoros
Phokas and Tsimiskes. And the picture that overshadows them all with
its radiance—the Empress Theophanó. Dramatic dialogue between
Augusta Theophanó and her three victims. A hymn to the exquisite
beauty of Theophanó, who symbolizes the ideal woman, at once savior
and destroyer. Even Kentaur, her Bulgar-Smasher son, arrives to
worship her.

In the Second Song, as in "The Widow's Son," the poet concentrates
on the hero's ancestors. Against a rich Byzantine background, the
Prinkipo Islands of the Bosporus, he paints the portraits of several
fascinating imperial personages, culminating in the devastating figure of
Empress Theophanó, the hero's mother. "The flute first sings of the
mother of the Bulgar-Slayer as though seeking the sources of his
might."[5] "Beautiful isles, tragic isles, the nine solitary islands. /...
Strange, mystical, mute and somber they are" (*Works* V, 36). Here are
famous monasteries, but also prisons for fallen emperors, victims of fate
"whose scales always move up and down." Here former wearers of
royal purple are now wrapped in the monk's coarse cloth, fixing their
glances in vain on the gleaming Golden City they lost.

In the deep solitude of naked Prote the poet brings to life, a
shadow's life, three Byzantine kings—Michael Rangavés, the hedonist
Lekapenós, and Romanos Diogenes—and the Empress Eiréne the
Athenian. Now, in the shadow of eternity, they pass their endless days
in contemplation and repentance. All this in preparation for the
appearance of the stunning mother of the hero.

> But whose mind will conceive you, who can imagine
> you, empress in your divine youth,
> standing apart, unmatched, alone, intoxicating the mind,
> turning a desolate path into an astral pass?
> ... What flute could fill
> with the breath of your song and not burst from it?
> Who can endure, who can survive to breathe in
> the snow-white lily, to drink its potent fragrance,
> sleep and death in one, something infinitely sweet,
> always desired here on earth.

... I know she was bathed
in the same waters that bathed ancient Helen,
among the kisses of reeds, among the burning longings of swans.

. . . .

I know that the voiceless, mindless Mothers
gave her the joy of Helen's grace.

Look! Augusta Theophanó! Beauty and Fury!
She holds a wand, a fine wand, cast
with a three-leaved silver lotus on its tip.
It is the lotus you never eat, the deadly herb
that ruins at sight, that melts you at the touch
and no matter who you are, reveler or ascetic,
everything you forget—life, power, youth;
honor if you are honorable, your throne if you are King;
and if you have riches a beggar you become and family deserter—
a child for her love, a killer for her kisses.

(*Works* V, 40—41)

This is the passion-consumed, perverse Theophanó. As one critic
writes:

Purple reflections create the face and body of Theophanó. A triple
purple cloak covers her body. The royal purple of her grandeur, the
Byzantine apostle-equal throne; the purple robe of murder, besplattered
with blood and groaning; and the purple of carnal passion, the flame,
the heaving, the swooning of the flesh—the flame of the body that
tastes and offers the deep pleasures.[6]

We see her mirrored in her three mighty lover-victims, in the shadows,
now dark now luminous, cast upon her life by history and legend. Here
the fifteen-syllable verse of Palamas reaches its ultimate beauty; it
vibrates with the nervous, gasping rhythm of carnal passion. We
commune with the dual flame of Byzantium, the carnal obsession, and
the holy fire of the soul. And it is the fear of the flesh that makes
carnal passion the overwhelming power that it is. Through Theophano
and the Byzantine interlocking struggle of carnality and spirituality,
Palamas is once again expressing his deepest self and his favorite theme.

In the dramatic dialogue between Theophanó and her victims we see
her multi dimensional character, her passions and intrigues. Romanos
II, the hero's father, was her first lover—victim.

Reveler, hunter, all-night prowler, rider,
for drink, for kiss—for all of love's
melting-sweet, mad, shining, empty things.

. . . .

The gardens of the Holy Palace know me—
how with roses I cover my profane revelings;
harbors, coves, castles and fields know me—
how I run after partridges, how I startle the deer,
how I catch the girls with my golden traps.

. . . .

But one morning, as I closed in on
a difficult-to-catch beast, lost
in a deep ravine, I met you at a cave's
entrance—our paths one fate.
And you enslaved me, you overpowered me.
Your child I am. Command.
My land now is in your flesh, my light in your eyes.

(Works V, 42–43)

He gave her everything. For her he destroyed his parents and his lovely
sisters, "whipping their flowering bodies with the coarse habit of the
nun." But the insatiable Theophanó eventually had enough of crazy
youth and longed to possess the graying, mature man, the hero who has
dedicated himself to the battlefield and to God, to Nikephoros Phokás.
And the man of duty and of faith, who preferred a cell on Holy Athos
to the crown of Augustus, falls on his knees and offers everything to
her. But he is old and jealous. Afraid of young lovers, he isolates
Theophanó from the world in "a great palace on the edge of the
wave—with triple, fourfold unscalable walls."

"And I stretched out and slept on the lion's skin.
And the lion more compassionate than your love.
You slaughtered me with Tsimiskés's sword. What do you want?"

"The other. Him who is my first pain, my last sickness.
You I only played with; him I worship.
I want the small-built man with the big eyes,
those blue, wet-glitter eyes that draw and drown me.
He looks like a blond child of Eros and in his heart
St. George rages and Digenes strikes.

(Works V, 45)

Tsimiskés is the one she really loves. And love is the only experience capable of touching, of elevating her corrupt, murderous nature.

> "On the altar of desire, the flesh day and night burns
> and, morning or evening, the kiss never ceases its singing.
> But the time of youth is only once, the great life once,
> and you, Love, once only struck like lightning in my heart's night.
> Love for the denier, for the deceiver love!"
>
> (*Works* V, 45)

After the murder of Nikephoros Phokás, Tsimiskés "repented" under pressure from Patriarch Polyeuktos. He sent Theophanó into exile. But her defeat, his separation from her, was his undoing. His great desire for her never died. In his anguish we see reflected the great power of Theophanó, seductress, enchantress, eternal woman. Even her son, the ruthless King, is drawn to her in her exile.

> So on the tragic islands, the solitary, lovely isles
> the queens of destruction and the kings of ruin
> leave their tombs, roam; their paths cross.
> They lament their sufferings and endlessly confess
> in the moonlight mists, in May's sweetness.
>
> . . . .
>
> And suddenly, a shrill trumpet sounds, the clatter of hooves,
> the army's din, and at the head a rider,
> man and horse one. He passes on
> as though coming to you, Theophanó, to bow,
> himself thirsty for your kiss, the King your son!
>
> (*Works* V, 46)

And the flute vows to continue its praise to Theophanó, no matter what others say about her. It will praise her for herself and for giving birth to her great son.

> . . . Glory!
> Glory to you Kentauress Queen, mother
> Who gave birth to the Kentaur King!
>
> . . . .
>
> And the arrow of Eros and the spear of Ares—
> it's hard to tell one from the other
> the moment when they strike hard or sturdily support
> the soul's and life's holy and unworthy things.

Seething Love and raging War,
uncontrollable horses that whinny and hoof-dig the ground.
A mother-fountain the woman and from her come
sin and salvation, resurrection and death—
the sword that slaughtered you, bold Nikephoros,
and the womb that bore you, Bulgar-Killer King!

(*Works* V, 47)

Once again Woman becomes, for Palamas, an all-encompassing symbol,
life itself, reconciling good and evil, destruction and regeneration.

III *Third Song*

Epic enumeration of the glorious path of the King through the castles,
plains and lakes of Macedonia. Wherever he stops, wherever he passes,
he smashes the Bulgarian. The spreading of his fame. He decides to go
on a pilgrimage to worship his patron Panaghia, the Virgin, to sing
hymns of victory to her, the Invincible Leader of Armies. He does not
stop at the great cities of Thrace and Macedonia—Edessa, Thessalonike—
not even in the Seven-Hilled City, Constantinople; not in Rome,
Antioch, Pergamos, Alexandria. He heads straight for Athens who wears
the Rock for a crown. Lyrical apotheosis of the Parthenon.

In the introductory poems and in the first two songs the hero has
been evoked, his legendary stature sketched, through association with
his ancestors and descendants, especially the mysterious shadows that
envelope the notoriety of his mother. In the Third Song he appears on
the epic scene directly and by reference to his deeds, the warrior's life.
This turn from the legendary to the concrete is signaled by a cascade of
place-names that are connected with the hero's military career. In
Thrace and Macedonia he conducted his most glorious campaigns. And
as he marches across this land each locality sings of his glory. "They
saw him, felt him, will never forget him/for everywhere he left his
lightning-marked path" (*Works* V, 49). Macedonia and her queen,
Thessalonike, become the poet's center of attention. This attention is
not accidental. When Palamas was writing the poem, Greece was torn
by the Macedonian Wars against the neighbors that Basil II had once
subdued. The liberation of Thessalonike was the nation's goal. Palamas
knows how to link his hero with the agony of the present: "Dead the
life-giving fires of the land."

The victorious campaigns of the King have ended, but his soul knows
no rest. Underneath the protective armor, "he feels the bite of the
hairshirt; feels it like an ascetic, a sinner." And he feels Mary's icon,

which he always carries as an amulet, touching his heart, "as if with fingers, insistently, turning to blood."

> He stopped, thought, longed to place
> a last jewel on his crown that glitters
> with rubies of war and devastation. He longed
> to add the pure pearl of compassion and prayer.
> What was it that moved him to this? God? Last Judgment?
> History? Salvation? His race? His soul?
> Who knows? . . .

(Works V, 51–52)

Who knows? Perhaps all of them: the mysterious questions that gnawed at the soul of the hero and of the poet.

And of all the glorious centers of Byzantium, of all of Mary's shrines, he chooses the shrine in the Parthenon–"Athens, you he loved; toward you he is coming." And the Flute-poet, too impatient to wait until his hero arrives in Athens, sings a hymn to the Parthenon:

> Are you the one who wears the rock for crown? Are you,
> Rock, supporter of the temple, the crown of the crown?
> Temple, who built you, beautiful in the heart of Beauty,
> for eternity, made you with every grace?
> In you rhythm is revelation, each line a Muse;
> Logos the marble has become, the idea art.
> And you have come to this miracle-land that meditates all . . .
>
> . . . .
>
> You were not built by enslaved mobs . . .
> You were raised with reason and with song
> where even the Law, the protector of Polis,
> came to life with rhythm, itself a song.
>
> . . . .
>
> And hear! When a man wants his youth again
> he must come to the river of beauty to bathe;
> to stand in the front of the beautiful
> and with all his heart to bow,
> worshiper, lover, singer, voyager–all.

(Works V, 55–56)

IV *Fourth Song*

It begins with an invocation to Greek Fire, the invincible weapon of the
Byzantines. The poet, with all the epic inspiration that lifts him widely
and tranquilly in the skies of the past, feels bound to a mystical
dream-stricken lyricism that holds him in a transporting lumination.
But he moves on, harmonizing elements that to the weak would seem
irreconcilable—his subjective self with the objective world, under the
clarifying influence of the epic rhythm of Kalliope. A detailed picturing
of fighters from many lands—the undefeated armies of the Bulgar-
Slayer. All are united by a common religious ideal—their faith in the
Lady of Vlaherna, at once Macedonian, Athenian and of the City of
Constantinople.

"The magic fire," "the liquid fire," "the winged fire," "the mystic
fire," "the Greek fire" that is sung in the opening lines of this song is
not only the dreaded weapon of the Byzantines. It becomes a symbol
of Basil's might and of Greek heroism. It is the undying fire that burns
in the heroic hearts and unifies the vast territories and heterogeneous
peoples that live under the doubleheaded eagle of Byzantium, the spirit
which unifies the great army that follows the hero on his pilgrimage.

Caesars, exarchs, magistri, domestics and dukes,

. . . .

Captains, aristocrats, humble born
they come from far and near, from the Dodecanese to Iceland.
. . . of every land and race, of every mind, heart and tongue,
birds from all directions and beasts from every corner,
all under one labarum, under one command,
sheltered by a single dream. And you, Idea, hold
them all, City of Bosporos, daughter of Constantine.

(Works V, 58)

Here follows a long catalogue of the units in the Emperor's army, an
epic description of their colors and character together with an
epigrammatic hymn of praise to their places of origin. Thus the poet
covers, with his sweeping verse, an area much more vast than the land
traversed by the hero on his way to Athens. This catalogue of armies is
consciously Homeric in manner and intention. And Palamas, the
song-ridden poet, has his own shield of Achilles wrought, a picture of
the richness of life presented in the great variety of song that soldiers of
different backgrounds sing.

> And they sing the fight of Digenes and Charon
> on marble threshing floors . . .
>
> . . . .
>
> And other soldiers sing their songs of the road;
> they sing of sea birds and mountain birds
> that always quarrel for feeding fields, and mountains and shores.
> And others sing the toils of the soldier, the victories of Kings.
>
> . . . .
>
> And others resound the sweetness of love's embraces
> the wreath-wedded wife, the honored home,
> the parting of the living—blacker than death—
> the pain of exile, the serpent of infidelity.
>
> (*Works* V, 63–64)

Songs of the Greek people, of the Greek past.

But the highest hymn is sung to the Virgin Mother toward whom they are journeying:

> Trumpets and conches break forth, rage;
> tambourines and tympani thunder and roar;
> and the valiant men's mouths burst and raise
> to heaven the Guiding Mother's hymn:
> Army-leading Lady, the victory chant for You!
> Whole peoples are weaving your hymn, like the wreath-maker,
> with a thousand palm leaves of glory, a myriad lilies of anguish,
> all for Your Grace, God-giver Theotokos!
>
> (*Works* V, 64)

It is this hymn that unifies the heterogeneous armies of Basil; it is the common faith and worship of the Virgin that holds together the vast mosaic of the Byzantine peoples.

V *Fifth Song*

It begins with an epigrammatic salutation to the beauty of the Greek earth. The King's crossing of Thessaly. The glory of the Thessalian plain. The flute, magic-possessed always, sings of the appearance of Faust, enchanted by Helen, on Thessalian soil. Faust's mythical entourage. Each locality with its tradition and history. The encounter of Parnassos; its address to the valiant armies of the Bulgar-Slayer. Parnassos-Liakura, the ancient and the modern name of the mountain—

the two names symbolizing the old and the new tightly entangled, the integrated Androgynos. Worshiping confession to the heroic personage of history, embodied by the Bulgar-Slayer on the unique Hellenic peak, and to Nature-Muse which is Parnassos.

The catalogue of armies is followed, in the fifth and sixth songs, by a catalogue of nature. As Basil enters Thessaly, nature acquires a new and deeper significance. Places here are not simply battle sites and natural scenery, as they were in Thrace and Macedonia. They are also Classical landscapes filled with ancient life, with history, mythology, art. Palamas here encounters, from a unique perspective, the entire Greek past—ancient, Byzantine, and modern—Hellenic reality in all its dimensions, nature, history, and spirit. And his hero is in motion, cutting across time, space, and values. The synthesis that is completed on the Akropolis begins here in the experience of Greek nature, the earth.

> Land of births, Greece, all moves in waves in you.
> A shore you are, always trembling, girding your calm,
> a woman's body and all things, from peaks to depths,
> bend lithely and dance, airlike and proud, yet seem still.
>
> All-swallowing Time swept over you
> and though it seems you changed your faith and your name
> . . . you are always Thessaly.
> In you gods and god-equals first sprang. You I greet!
> . . . Greetings to you!
> Like your rich-seeded soil, Imagination conceived
> in you, fused in bliss with Hellenic mind,
> and bore lovely Greek children—the Myths.
>
> (*Works* V, 70)

Greek reality—the Hellenic Idea, Hellenic culture—cannot be experienced, cannot be understood apart from Greek nature. The best initiation into the spirit of Hellenism is through the Greek earth. And the synthesis of Hellenism that Palamas molds in *The King's Flute* is concretely, organically based on the experience of Greek nature.

The correspondence of nature and spirit is so significant in Palamas that it shapes a fundamental principle of his *Poetics*: "I know that the natural world is for the creative imagination nothing but a symbol of the spiritual world and the greater the poet is the more correspondences he finds between the spiritual and the natural realms."

In the process of establishing the relationship between nature and spirit the poetic myth is born. "Nature, advancing toward the soul, becomes myth. And myth is inseparable from the two elements it fuses. Myth is action, but not historical action as in history; it is symbolic, inner action."[8] *The King's Flute,* a vast panorama of Greek nature and Greek history is, precisely, a monumental symbol of Hellenism.

In the mythical reweaving of history time restrictions are disregarded. Greek mythology and post-Byzantine history, the Olympus of Zeus and the Olympus of klephts, the Battle of Thermopylae and the Byzantine Wars, are all swept in the poet's vision of Hellenism. Even Faust's descent into the Classical past is included, a great moment in the history of poetry. And the prophetic Flute sings all.

Each glorious spot of the Greek earth comes alive as the great King passes over it and the magic Flute resurrects its glory. Mountains, rivers, crags, passes, all reverberate in the flute's sound; Olympus "a hiding place of gods and guerrila fighters," the pass of Thermopylae, "widened by the Spartan King and the bodies of the three hundred," made a world. But of all localities Parnassos stands apart. Here the poet stops to add a significant elaboration to the synthesis he has conceived. In response to the Flute the mountain picks up the song, first speaks of itself and then addresses the hero-King:

> "Double are my peaks and double my name;
> old-man Parnassos I am, and Liakura the youth—
> man and woman in one, a joined pair,
> inseparable, a world, a creation;
> I harmonize things that seem unjoinable.
> I am man-world and woman-creation; I am an ancient world,
> a new sun always among the stars of the mind-filled heavens.
> The two purest elements, light and water,
> took flesh here, became creatures, became creators—
> one rose as god, was named Apollo,
> the other became goddess
> and she is Muse, ninefold, nine-souled, nine times mother."
>
> (*Works* V, 76)

And as he speaks, intoxicated by his own speech, Parnassos becomes less and less the remote Classical past, less and less the symbol, until he leaps up, dances and sighs like a modern, living Greek, a guerrila fighter, a shepherd, a poverty-tormented man, the mountain-spirit of freedom, the struggle for survival on the barren mountains of Greece, in a barren universe:

> The crags are my fortresses, the firs my army;
> the birds are my people, the eagles my commanders.

. . . .

... Nothing have I scorned. I am proud
of a sheep-pen as I would be of a temple.
And I hear the cuckoo bird's song with the same religious startle
that I hear above me the clouds' battling and lightning.

. . . .

But I have my sorrows, and my gnawing thoughts,
nights that never dawn, enigmas with no answers.

. . . .

And within me is heard again the world's deep dirge,
bitter and loud, from a myriad tongues.

(*Works* V, 78)

Here Palamas once again identifies his tormented self with the struggles
and agonies of his people and of mankind.

"And who are you?" the living mountain asks the passing soldiers.
And they answer: "We ourselves don't know who we really are. But call
us orphans of Greece, Fate's bastards." They describe themselves in
terms of the life and exploits of klephts rather than of Byzantine
warriors. For Palamas and his contemporaries the spirit of 1821 is the
most heroic, the most immediate to their lives. And the mountain
welcomes them as though welcoming resistance fighters:

> "Welcome pallikaria!
> I am Parnassos, still, and now Liakura.
> And I am always that temple
> that God never abandons, no matter what his name."

(*Works* V, 80)

He invites them, who are "led by their unbending Hero," to worship
whatever god they choose; all gods are "closer when one prays from my
peaks."

VI *Sixth Song*

The march toward the eastern region of the mainland continues.
Livadia with Helikon. Thebes with her Ascrean bard. Hymn to the
living popular names that replaced the classical counterparts.

Intoxicated by the hymn to Parnassos in the Fifth Song the poet
continues to paint lyrically the landscape east of Parnassos as the march

toward Athens continues. But a pattern of contrasts dominates the lyrical description: on the one hand, idyllic, undying elements—"water-mothers, fountains, splashing springs, foams, dew pourings, waves and snakes"—and on the other hand human creations that fall to ruin:

> And here and there, on all sides, remnants and ruins
> that once were castles and temples, citadels and cities,
> and are no more, half-there, half-fallen;
> only Nature stands, speaking to all, always.
>
> (*Works* V, 83)

Another contrast is drawn between the mountain people—health, heroism, freedom—and the folk of the plains, subservient, "numb-souled," given to collective habits.

The passing army sees Thebes "crippled by evils pitilessly heaped upon her . . . by devastating warriors." But these crude military men, whose "ears are trained to hear only the trumpet's sounds," do not hear the song of the Ascrean:

> the singer who wanders after nightfall, wailing;
> who passes by Dirke's waters and mingles his bitter tears
> with the murmuring springs, muddling the clear water.
> He laments his fallen Thebes for he, the chosen
> son of song, has the gift to tell what time holds—
> the past, the future, the now. He weeps for
> life's torments, the decadence of man, the falseness
> of woman, the bitterness of toil, the cruelty of Nature.
>
> (*Works* V, 85–86)

The Ascrean, beloved poetic ancestor of Palamas, becomes once again a singer of the ages of man, this time of the fate of the Greek. The song ends, as if to dispel the gloom, with a lyrical hymn to demotic names that adorn Greek things.

VII *Seventh Song*

Athens, souled by the fusion of Athena and Aphrodite, shudders as she awaits the miracle, the appearance of the King. Nature and history are painted in unison. They are called to life. The rock with the magic of art adorning it—still intact—a City in marble. Pantheism is mystically interpreted by the poet. The rock, a ghostly watchman, seems to be expecting to see, in turn, Julian the Apostate, Alaric, Dexippos, the last seven philosophers of Athens, Athena herself, barbarian conquerors—Haus, Scythians, Slavs. But it sees none other than the Bulgar-Slayer, Lyrical apotheosis of the King—Ares is coming to pay a visit to Aphrodite who now inhabits the Rock.

Athens is Palamas's city. He lived there from the age of seventeen until he died. He knows every detail, every ornament of Athens; he knows her beauty, her esthetic essence. He has sung her innumerable times. But this is a unique occasion. Athens is of supreme importance to the myth of the poem. Palamas mobilizes his poetic resources and rises to the occasion. The esthetic essence of Athens and Attic nature is captured first:

> Morning, the day sunstreamed and sunbeautiful,
> Athens a sapphire stone on the earth's ring.
> Light everywhere, always the light, and light reveals all;
>
> . . . .
>
> Great and humble things, all shine the same.
> Pentele's peak and the little asphodel,
> the bright-crowned temple and the pale anemone,
> all weigh the same on the scale of creation.

(Works V, 89)

The poet becomes possessed by his subject and continues to sing a hymn to the Rock that contains the essence of Palamas's attitude toward Classical Greece. The hymn is six pages long, and one feels that the epic narrative is completely interrupted. But nothing less will do. Palamas has a whole world of impressions within himself, visual impressions of the landscape he is painting and cultural impressions of Classical Hellenism. They become song, symbol, rock, the Rock upon which the tide of the Byzantine Emperor, representative of his culture, will break. And as Palamas paints Attic nature he depicts the Classical soul, its beauty and meaning. And he sees the Classical soul, primarily, as art and through art. The Rock with its brilliance and its temples becomes the symbol of Classical Greece and the Propylaea that leads into its essence. Palamas describes the statues and reliefs of the Parthenon as they exist, in their true measure, and then draws their symbolic extension.

The Parthenon and the Rock of the Akropolis are first depicted as immortal art, a marble ideal world. Later they stir and come alive, as the poet sees the living miracle of the Classical civilization. This is masterfully evoked by the description of the Panathenean procession as it waves and stirs across the span to its destination.

> And the procession is always about to begin and hasn't yet;
> it is that sweet, restless moment of excitement,

> the living moment that you always seek and wait for
> and return to, glad that there is no other
> such as this. And you are happy,
> not for the moment you possess but the one you expect.
>
> (*Works* V, 92)

This is a living dream. But the dream is suddenly interrupted as the Rock, the eye of Athens and the poet's vantage point, sees a moving darkness on the horizon, toward Eleusis:

> the mystic litany toward Wisdom's City,
> something like a dust storm, look! a darkening cloud
> that advances and rises and grows,
> in this brilliance of light darkening even more . . .
>
> (*Works* V, 94—95)

The contrast here between the luminous Classical realm and the dark Byzantine soul is obvious. And the Rock, troubled—as though a new civilization, a new cosmogonic wave threatened it—wonders what army is advancing toward Athens: is it "the last prophet of the Sun," Julian the Apostate, "to restore my broken altars;" is it "Alaric returning" or perhaps Dexippos, "the last child of this land," to save her? Hope and terror, the fate of Greece throughout the ages.

As the advancing army approaches the Rock begins to see details:

> The sweat of a thousand roads drips from their bodies;
> in their glances the fires of a thousand wars burn,
> a crowd difficult to measure, daring . . .
>
> . . . .
>
> Their leader an unbending giant rider
> who stands apart among them and, though one,
> is worth the whole multitude . . .
>
> (*Works* V, 98)

One look at the great hero is enough to transform the agonized questioning of the Rock to awe and admiration;

> Noble is his face and noble his soul's icon;
> joy shines in his eyes and their look
> is straight, pure, free of deception
>
> . . . .

and over the arch of his clear brow,
Thought is the leader, Pride the judge;
the moon's gleam on his face and from his shoulder
a fine column rises, his strong neck.

. . . .

his spreading beard a gold and silver thicket,
and when a quake of anger disturbs his thought
the hand thrusts upward and grips it,
as though in his fury he seeks a firm hold.

                                                           (*Works* **V**, 99)

The Rock has been scanning the horizon, hoping that a hero from
the past—Athena, Philosopher, Dexilaos—will appear to restore its
Classical grandeur. But since no such personage appears, the Rock turns
to the Byzantine King and apotheosizes him. This mighty man will at
least insure the immortality of the Hellenic Idea, in new garments, in
new forms:

"Let me call him Olympian, let me shout: 'You are Ares!'
To cry out: 'Ares you are though you come from wild,
foreign lands, and barbarian you look—but are not.

. . . .

You are Ares and you have come enclosing
in your heart, with a new vigor, the same Greece.
And deeper still you hide in your heart
an arrow-wound of Eros, a wound that burns and
drives you to Aphrodite. You longed for her
and they told you: "Aphrodite lives on the Rock."
You come.' "

                                                          (*Works* **V**, 100)

As Emilios Hourmouzios writes:

The war-tossed hero comes to Athens to find a mate for his soul, as the
war-thirsty Ares longs for his mate, Aphrodite. Athens, too, fallen and
decadent, living with the bitter memory of her days of grandeur and her
valiant leaders, awaits with erotic shudders the manly embrace of the
hero. She is disillusioned with the pale philosopher "who leans over the
graves" and longs for a new flowering of life. The might of the
Bulgar-Slayer promises this flowering. And she is ready to give herself
to him, expecting the power of deeds to redeem her from the decline of
logos.[9]

VIII *Eighth Song*

Depiction of the dying paganism in Athens, Proklos, the last
Neoplatonic philosopher. Pallas Athena seeks sanctuary in his house.
Asclepigeneia, the last pagan prophetess. By contrast, the worship and
miracles of the Virgin are depicted in the monasteries of the Near East.
The story of the painter with lilies.

> But Aphrodite is marble now, Kore a phantom. Rock,
> a cold mystic fear binds your speech
> and all the gods and heroes you carry
> are phantoms, too; all marble.

(Works V, 100)

The new faith and the new way of life have rooted deeply and have
replaced the old gods, the pagan spirit. But to portray the dying of
paganism dramatically and fully Palamas goes back to the fifth century
and brings to life historical figures and events. Proklos, the last
Neoplatonic philosopher, is visting Athens to worship Athena:

> . . . Lykios Proklos, the last prophet of the pagans,
> so beautiful, the likeness of the god of day
> who came to live on earth, a shepherd for a king.
> But he found your fortress closed and guards outside;
> everything dried out, desolate, without soul or sound.

(Works V, 101)

Only the storks, "resting on the ruined temples," speak to him:

> "Stranger, your Pallas was driven off by another Lady,
> solitary, unarmed, from far away, now perched here,
> untouched, grieved, as though choking under her red veil.
>
> . . . .
>
> If only she outstretched her hand all fell to their knees,
>
> . . . .
>
> She had only to glance and under her eyes
> marble, men and gods, melted, crumbled away."

(Works V, 102)

Ploklos listens and then silently goes away, "deep in thought." He
returns to his little house at the foot of the Rock, and there he remains
awake, deeply troubled. Everything around him seems to lament for the
death that he feels in his soul. But suddenly, at midnight, there is a
knock at his door. Athena has come to seek sanctuary for the night:

> "I have no place to go; no place to pass the night.
> Put me somewhere here to rest and tomorrow, at dawn,
> I'll flee with the swallows and the cranes."
>
> (*Works* V, 102)

Here Palamas's double soul, the Christian and the pagan, lives its
most dramatic moments. He identifies completely with Proklos and
suffers the tragic agony that is in the heart of Hellenic fate:

"And Proklos, who embodies the grief of centuries of Greek life,
speaking with the tongue of all men of the mind who lived under the
fountainhead of Logos, who breathed in the flowering of pagan Greek
thought . . and beauty, offers to the goddess his soul—an indestructible
home—today a grave but tomorrow her fortress again. For Proklos
believes that one day in the stream of centuries, Logos will again demand its inalienable rights."[10]

> "And the world, orphaned without you, will know you once again,
> in a greater, renewed youth.
> Exile may sweep you, but not death.
> You are the Lady of the past and of the future."
>
> (*Works* V, 103)

> And with the first light of dawn the goddess leaves, like a mist.
> And she never returned. No one saw her again.
> But you, Lady of the present, perhaps of all time,
> Lady of Golden Laurels, great is your Grace!
>
> (*Works* V, 104)

After the depiction of the Classical side of Hellenism, Palamas turns,
even more passionately, to paint its antithesis, the Christian spirit. And
as there was a human counterpart to Athena, Proklos, so there is one
for the Virgin, the Monk. Through the Monk, Palamas penetrates the
depths of the Byzantine soul, the essence of Byzantine faith.

A magnificent, ancient monastery is described with brilliant detail. It
stands on a steep slope in Lebanon where it "grew immense with the
cedars." This is the heart of the Near East where the worship of the

Virgin began. Outside the monastery the beauty and tranquillity of nature, within the soul's abandonment to worship, "to ceaseless prayer and chant." The heart of the monastery is the domed church inside which the Monk ceaselessly paints the life of the Virgin. She is his greatest passion, his only passion. His life is endless devotion to her, his work endless recounting of her life, especially the supreme moment of Annunciation. His only speech is, "the two-word song in all the tones of the psalm: Hail, Graced-One!"

So the Monk lives his days, "gentle and patient, obedient and calm," until he is no longer able to lift his brush to paint his beloved. All he is able to do now is to fall on his knees, in front of Her icon, and "murmur the two-word song . . ." until the moment of his death. The earth that receives him becomes fragrant, and all creation surrounding the monastery is "like a lush, incredible spring."

> And one time in a brilliant April,
> a prodigal May, during the novena prayers,
> the great miracle came: a white lily burst from the fragrant grave.
> And on the lily leaves gold written words shone: Hail, Graced-One.
>
> (*Works* V, 111)

The monks dig the grave, trace the lily stalk. It leads to the mouth of the Monk, its root to his heart. And inside the heart they see painted the Virgin's image.

> Graced Lady, hail!
> Mother of the despairing, protectress of all,
> before you the hopeless, the whole world are one.
>
> . . . .
>
> The first world, that rich world, was choked by you,
> and from it the gold written lily grew.
>
> . . . .
>
> And now the world is like the mouth of a buried saint,
> flower pot of a mystic lily, and in the world's heart—
> from the unknown ascetic to the Bulgar-Slayer,
> the victor who is climbing to worship you—
> are You, Mother of God, in brilliance painted!
>
> (*Works* V, 111)

In these final lines of the Eighth Song Palamas becomes one with the collective soul of Greek Christianity. His verse resounds with hymns of exaltation to Panaghia, constantly echoing the Byzantine hymns of worship that through the centuries accompanied and determined the religious vision and life of the Greeks. The portraits are completed:

With his two symbols, Proklos and the Monk, the poet has given us the essence of the two opposing worlds. He showed us, on the one hand, the dream and the emotions of the pagan and, on the other, the unworldly turn of the hermit. On the one side the pain for the beauty that is fleeting like mist and on the other the ecstasy and the mystery that fall like heavenly dew. Here the passion of wisdom, there the calm eros of the metaphysical. Here the sun, joy, quivering earth; there religious awe, patience, vision of the immaterial.[11]

It is a dramatization and exaltation of antithetical modes of life, not their synthesis.

IX *Ninth Song*

Again and always to the Doric temple. Inside the Parthenon. Satiric attack on the "learned" tradition that stands for backward narrow-mindedness. The King's prayer to the Virgin of Athens, Panaghia. The entire life of the Emperor, all his adventures and trials, unfolds. Everything seems to pass in front of his eyes, quick and sparkling as in lightning. His thoughts and his deeds. The King is a type of Superior Man, a hero of might who becomes to himself, according to the circumstances, the law itself. His minister of State, his generals—Vardas Phokás and Vardas Sklerós (the Hard).

"And always the Doric temple, simple and immense." The poet suddenly, as though arriving with Basil's army, sees the Parthenon and is startled or, better still, shocked by the sight. The temple's simplicity is monstrously deformed "by the blind eye and harsh hand of the Nazarene." Its fine "polytheistic brow" is marred by the travesty of the Byzantine dome. The poet, who in the preceding song identified passionately with the Monk, is now outraged by the profanation of the Classical ideal. He is now the post-Byzantine Greek who seeks to restore both realities to life, who loves both ideals:

No matter how fervently the ecstatic faith of the Monk may stir in him, the poet is not a Byzantine. He is a contemporary Greek, cleansed of the blind religious fanaticism. His consciousness is capable of fusing his Christianity and his paganism, striving to enjoy in this marriage the offspring of the new beauty of his century. He has the strength to be a Christian and at the same time to be moved by the flowering of the ancient spirit.[12]

Naturally he laments when he sees the perverted Parthenon:

> So a barbaric King, the great Constantine,
> became Apollo's headsman, beheaded the beautiful god.
> And on the headless body of marble, that harmonious body,
> he placed his own royal head–an idol.
> And look! The statue that was the joy of the world is now a monster!
>
> *(Works* V, 112)

In describing the transformation of the Doric temple to a Byzantine church Palamas once again depicts the nature of the new religion and at the same time the relentless historical law that determines the life and death of civilizations. He sees the Parthenon as the heart of Greece and reflector of her historic fate:

> Each time Fate pitilessly
> strikes at the Race,
> the heart of the Race, the temple,
> will first take the blow,
> will shake and deeply crack.
>
> . . . .
>
> The Byzantine will turn the temple Christian,
> the Frank will make it Catholic,
> the Moslem will force it to wear the turban;
> each race will plunder it with rage.
>
> . . . .
>
> Until–who will believe it?–
> a last master, the scholar, will stick on the holy ruin
> like a leech, and defile it.
>
> *(Works* V, 112–3)

The last three lines are directed against the contemporary purists and their empty love for the past.

A detailed picture of the transformed temple is presented here, intended to evoke the character of Byzantine esthetics and spirituality. The Byzantine additions to the temple have covered its naked beauty, have blocked out the radiance of the Attic sun, but have not

completely succeeded in obliterating the pagan surge of life that the
glorious marble depicts. From an ancient throne across the pulpit:

> The marble sphinxes, always inscrutable,
> gaze at the golden angels; and a winged woman
> hiding in the prickly vine
> shows her pagan face, her startled eye.

(Works V, 114)

The lover of pagan beauty once again laments the death of Classical
beauty, after the "barbaric invasion" of the Christian religion. Yet the
new Lady, now enthroned in the temple, does not leave him
untouched. Once the lament for the ancient spirit is sung, the poet can
let the other part of his soul turn to the most consummate personage
and symbol of Christianity, the Panaghia, the patron saint of his hero.

The Bulgar-Slayer arrives at the temple. The epic voyage-march is
now complete and with it the journey through historical Hellenism. Up
to this point, the poet's attention has focused on the hero's
countenance and deeds. From here on the concentration will be on
revealing his soul. And confession is the supreme mode of inner
revelation.

The Emperor, burdened by his awesome duties and torn by his
conflicts, has come to confess, to unburden his soul in front of the
soothing Lady of Compassion. After a lifetime of struggle against
innumerable enemies his hardened, relentless soul longs to com-
municate his pain and his vision. In a silent prayer to Panaghia he
reveals his deepest torments:

> And his prayer is strange, bearing on its wings
> a war loving flame and a mystic dew.
> Double-visaged he stands, a monk and a warring hero.
> The black habit presses upon his golden armor
> and two unreconcilable drives merge in his prayer.
> The first, a mighty life. Inside him worldly cares
> turn, glitter, groan, are always born.
> The second scatters ecstatic dreams . . .
> white incense from a golden burner.
>
> . . . .
>
> The King prays in silence. A soul.

(Works V, 115)

The   hero   recalls   his   past,   his   youth   spent   in   passion,   his apprenticeship in government under his tutor Basil the Eunuch, president of the Council, and his long years of war and strife. He fought against invaders who constantly threatened the empire and against internal enemies—relatives, generals, high officials—who sought to undermine his power. He has known all the cruelties of battle and the cold-blooded machinations and intrigues of the palace. From all his struggles he emerged victorious, and now, at the peak of life, he stands mighty and solitary, determined to take final stock of himself, to bare his soul to the Lady of Athens. His "blood-begotten spirit," to use Yeats's phrase, longs to be gathered "into the artifice of eternity." His confession is both a need and a culminating act of self-conquering and self-knowledge.

As the long confession of the King unfolds, in this and in the following two songs, we see once again Palamas's complex method of synoptic presentation. His hero is the great personage of history who shapes the destinies of peoples and determines the course of events; he is a mirror of Byzantine life and culture and, finally, a reflection of the poet's own personality and mission. The second element, the search into the Byzantine soul and culture, is here the dominant concern. In these three songs we see the Byzantine spirit with all its conflicts and torments; we witness the unceasing battles of worldly and spiritual forces. The great war hero becomes the embodiment of human struggle exemplified by every mode of external and internal conflict. Strife is his very essence; the preservation of the empire and the salvation of his soul are his supreme duties and goals. Mingled with the glitter of imperial power, the intrigues and the bloody battles, we see the monastic yearning, the spiritual flame gasping for the absolute under the guidance of the gentle protectress of Byzantine Christendom he has come to worship. This is a great dramatic moment: to witness the hardened, ruthless, superhuman soul of the mighty warrior transformed into that of a humble worshiper of the Lady of Grace and Compassion; to see pity, love, and humility suddenly blooming in his praying soul. Here, naked before us, is the paradoxical nature of man comsumed by the fire of Christian faith. The beast in him, the greed for power, the madness of materiality and carnality, are incessantly opposed by the yearning for grace, by humility, by the spiritual passion for God. The warrior and the mystic, the killer and the saint live in one heart. One thinks of Dostoevsky and the terrible ambivalence of man. Palamas is torn by this ambivalence, the Passion and the Dream, and here he adds to it the sharpness and power of its Byzantine counterpart.

At the culminating moment of his life, this hour of confession, which coincides with attaining self-knowledge, the King is able to offer himself, his entire being, to Panaghia, as he had given himself wholly to the Byzantine state throughout the years of struggle:

> And I became the black-clothed monk of deeds that
> always moves on, with the cross in hand and the sword.

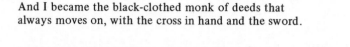

> Mind and soul, flesh and visage, all a polyphonic
> harmony which endures unchanged. And I am the arch-singer,
> myself . . .

(Works V, 122)

Palamas, too, understands his complex fate and mission: he is a poet but also a teacher and leader of his people. And he, like his hero, gave his whole being to his gods, to Poetry and to Greece.

X *Tenth Song*

Epic characterization of Vardas Sklerós and Vardas Phokás. The King's sympathy for the living, demotic elements; his revulsion toward the "learned" and the archaic-minded. Hymn to the demotic tradition. Hymnic arrangement of the grace of the Virgin in all her exalted names.

The King's prayer continues uninterruped in this and in the Eleventh Song. Here the King recalls two devastating events of his reign, the rebellion of two of his greatest generals, Vardas Sklerós and Vardas Phokás. He relates and dramatizes their rebellions and the great danger he faced before he crushed the insurgents. As he depicts the might and nature of his adversaries he juxtaposes his own strength and moral principles which account for his victories over all his enemies. We see him once again as a complex personage of great moral and spiritual resources, not only as a mighty warrior. He is a man of wisdom, schooled by experience and struggle, and a man of faith and pious devotion. As he exalts his values and identifies with the healthy elements of his world we see the poet once again wearing the mask of his hero, manifesting his ideals and praising the demotic tradition. A little out of character, perhaps, the King sings another of Palamas's hymns to the demotic language and life:

> My enemy is the false wisdom of the learned, and all the
> assassins of life and stiflers of truth. Evil growths are

these grammarians, orators, philosophers with the blown-up
titles and the empty heads, weavers of airy words and singers
of nonsense.

. . . .

The tongue that thunders when I speak is the tongue of laborers,
of fighters, of whole men, a tongue never akin to your speech,
your colorless, embalmed words.

(Works V, 195–96)

Another essential dimension of Basil, his religious faith, is focused
upon next, and its origins and strengthening are explained. When he was
fighting Vardas Phokás, ready for single combat, the rebel, as history
and legend tell us, fell from his horse, dead at the feet of his King. In
the poem, Basil, like Byzantine religious superstition, attributes the
destruction of his adversary to a miracle, the intervention of the Virgin,
Protectress of the Empire. From this moment on the King's faith in the
Virgin and his devotion to her will never cease or weaken.

And I felt your icon on my breast stirring with life, becoming
my soul. And since then I am always in deep thought as though
that moment struck me forever. . . .
And from that time it's as though I have the eyes of a bird
which can pierce the dark and see in the night.

(Works V, 129)

This account of the King's awakening to profound faith elucidates
popular Byzantine faith and religious superstition, as well. His devotion
to Panaghia embodies the religious essence of Byzantium, and the hero
once again becomes the mirror of a whole culture. Accordingly, the
hymnic crescendo that ends this song is cast in the finest devotional
language of the tradition, a language so rich and exalted that it
completely defies attempts at translation.

XI *Eleventh Song*

The prayer to the Mother of Mercy continues. The triumphant tone
changes to that of lament. Melancholy from the contemplation of the
future. The phantom and the Apocalypse. The vision of unborn time.
The decline and destruction of the Seven-Hilled City. The Frankish
occupation. The Turk. Modern times. Europe, mistress and leader of
civilization. The emergence of America. The new Atlases. The fear of
the Yellow Races. At the distant background the stunning march of

Mammon and Poorlion, the two unreconcilable forces—capitalist and worker. The might of science that destroys myths. Only Aphrodite-Love and Athena-Wisdom are saved from the universal destruction. Through the mouth of the heroic King who becomes leader and guardian of the Hellenic fatherland, the poet unfolds his philosophy of Hellenism. Eternal recurrence, ceaseless transformation in the tempo of rise and decline. Everything changes; nothing is lost. If we must have gods they will be, above all, War and Violence. The triple-phantom vanishes. The prayer ends in humble devotion to the Virgin and the Lord.

The Eleventh Song is the culmination of the poem. The vast epic torrents of the introductory and the first ten songs—the rich historical, religious, and lyrical streams—converge here in an intense apocalyptic vision. The poem's hero, till this point portrayed as a man of action and burning religious faith, now becomes a thoughtful visionary contemplating the historical fate of Hellenism and of mankind. He yields to the temptation of thought, to a philosophical view of history. All that he has learned from his long life of struggle in the worldly dominion, all that he has intuited in his solitary mystical life is now concentrated in a prophetic vision. And for dramatic and philosophical reasons the vision is presented in two parts, by a revealing Angel who speaks to the King, and by the King himself in reply.

As he was leaning on the Palace window one day, looking at the beautiful Bosporus, Basil notices an awesome Angel near him.

> He touched me and I trembled. He breathed in my
> eyes and I saw. One of his wings was like a copper
> writing tablet and on it shone all that Destiny wrote.
> His other wing was like a magic mirror in which the
> unborn times darkly spoke.
>
> (*Works* V, 133)

The phantom-angel has three changing aspects in his appearance. Sometimes he looks like an angel of God, sometimes like "the archangel of the abyss," and at other times he resembles Basil's namesake, his chief counselor. A dissonant humming rises from the phantom, and "itself triple," speaks to the King in a mysterious prophetic voice. It tells of the glory of Byzantium and of Basil's triumphs, all things which have happened already. Then it speaks of the future of the empire and the enemies who will overrun it and destroy it. The brave defenders and sages of Byzantium will flee to the West, as in *The Dodecalogue of the Gypsy,* there to kindle a new civilization. Europe then will rise as the leading power and culture, while the Hellenic world will decline and live in slavery and darkness.

In the next cycle of decline and rise of civilizations, the New World, America, will succeed Europe. The lost Atlantis will rise from the ocean, and new Atlases will be born to rule mankind:

> "Tell, o Ocean depths, what welling up is this?
> Aphrodite rising a second time?"—"Aphrodite? No.
> We are bringing Atlantis in the sun again, the dream-
> beautiful island which is itself a world."
>
> Athens is no more. Europe now exists. Give her, o
> Europe, give from your vitals to her who is born again.
>
> . . . .
>
> And look! The Atlases, the Atlases! They come, are
> sown, are.
> And they grow—giants, free, rearing to conquer, lords
> of the new world, dread of the old.

(Works V, 138)

But, in spite of the promise of health and justice, the New World soon becomes the dominion of Greed. The great monster Mammon—the Antichrist, "serpent and eagle in one"—is the lord-oppressor of the world. Then, after centuries of injustice and exploitation, the time comes for this evil ruler to pay for his crimes, "pay with the wealth that once the whole earth couldn't store."

> Mangled poor people, blackfated poor people,
> you were like driftwood on the sand, a reed on the plain.
> But light struck and you knew yourself. Enough!
> Rise dragonstrong working class! Attack, worker! Avenge!
> And see! the mightiest uprising on the earth—
> the rising of the poor!

(Works V, 139)

Mammon falls, and Poorlion, the proletariat, rises to become the new master of the earth. And now:

> . . . Peace in the world,
> brotherhood among all peoples, joy and good will on earth!
> Work is now thrice noble to all and the world one Republic!

(Works V, 140)

The old privileges, values, gods are swept away in the cataclysmic rise of the new order. Only Athena-Wisdom and Aphrodite-Love survive to reign in the universe. We are again in the ideological climate of the last songs of *The Dodecalogue of the Gypsy*. Palamas is still gripped by the optimistic science-socialism ideal of his earlier period.

The Angel's humming noise ceases, and the King who has been listening overwhelmed replies to this temptation of optimism and internationalism with his own vision of history. The word temptation is of key importance here. The Angel's vision, with its dominant optimistic and messianic elements, offers an attractive theory regarding the future of mankind, a promise of harmony and liberation from ordeals and agonies for leaders and masses alike. But the man of action, the leader, is by nature watchful, not to be lured by intellectual formulations and dreams. He relies above all else on his experience and clings to his nature and mission. This attitude of the King, implicit in his character, leads him to counter the Angel's vision with his own philosophy of history. As a Byzantine emperor and the embodiment of the Byzantine ideals, he cannot accept the notion that the empire will vanish, that the glory he achieved through his titanic struggles and sacrifices will be swept away by time. To him, the Byzantine state and its ideals are permanent and immutable. And it is this faith that enables him to counter the awesome vision of the revealing Angel with a force and clarity surprising even to himself.

There is above all, the King replies, the law of eternal recurrence. All things, all events are only transformations of things and events that always existed. The fundamental nature and structure of things and societies will never change. There will always be shapers of history. There will always be war: the struggle for power and supremacy within nations and among nations. War and violence are the eternal forces in the world. And the King identifies himself with war, with unceasing strife and with might. And it is this warlike flame that will secure the survival of the race, of Hellenism. Basil becomes one with the spirit of Hellenism and proclaims that the race will live on, no matter how mighty its enemies, how devastating their attacks. There will always be a resurrection after each death.

> And I said: Wherever the Greek spirit breathes,
> wherever Greece is crucified, the Greeks triumph;
> where there is resistance, cross, watch, sword, road
> I will be there, myself: a spirit returning to life,
> a skeleton and I will always sing the epic song.
>
> (*Works* V, 144)

In the two antithetical views of the world, the Angel's and the King's, we again find Palamas's own divided outlook: optimism and pessimism, socialistic thought coexisting with the cult of the hero, harmony and warlike strife. The intellectual drama of his own life is powerfully cast in this song.

The King's vision as it is formulated is necessary here. It serves several poetic, nationalistic, and psychological purposes. First of all, the poem must end with an exaltation of the hero's personality and nature. His personal, unique vision is organically fitting in the poem and in Greek history. The reality of the hero's and the poet's life is one of strife and war. Heroism and a warlike spirit are needed to preserve the Hellenic heritage and to inspire Palamas's contemporaries to action for social reconstruction and territorial growth. The poem ends, fittingly, in the heroic tone needed "to make brothers of dreams and deeds" and to kindle "the dead creative fires across the land." But since the hero is still speaking to the Virgin, in confession, his last lines are again a prayer:

> The triple phantom vanished, a mist. But sin, a stone.
> I beg you All Holy One. My pain is deep.
> You are the harbor of sinners, the joy of the world.
> Pity, my Lady. Extinguish the flame of blasphemy inside me.
> Temptation has visited me, raised me to the heights
> and from the summits showed me the realms
> of the world, with all their sins and monsters.
> And I did not seal my ears, did not close my eyes.
> I became an opposer to the words of Temptation.
> Mercy, o Lord! May your will be done.

> *(Works* V, 145)

XII *Twelfth Song—"Heroic Trilogy"—"Epilogue"*

The scene as in the first song. Preparation for the funeral of the glorious Skeleton with all royal honors. Michael Paleologos himself stretches his hands toward the holy relic. But, as he touches it, it crumbles to the ground. The Flute falls, a mute reed. The Magic is broken.

In its entirety the poem is epico-lyric, or better, an epic Hymn, comparable to the Homeric hymns—with the difference that the Flute's hymn embraces the entire world with its hero.

The last song is only fifty lines long and in low key. Silence, quietness, and awe follow the great polyphonic song of the magic Flute. The poet quickly sketches the contrast between the heroic world he has created and actuality. Nothing more is needed.

Critical opinion on *The King's Flute* has been mixed ever since the time of its publication. Most of the negative criticism has found the poem excessively rhetorical and, as a result, tiresome to read. Popular opinion seems to agree on this point. The popularity of *The King's Flute* never approached that of *The Dodecalogue of the Gypsy* and of several other works of Palamas. Recent criticism, however, has re-examined the poem and has often found it equal to *The Dodecalogue.* There is no doubt that *The King's Flute* is one of Palamas's greatest works; as the critic E. Papanoutsos writes, "It is the greatest epic of the endurance and continuity of Hellenism."[13]

Palamas included four additional poems in the first edition of *The King's Flute.* The first three, collectively titled "The Heroic Trilogy," are related to the major poem in spirit only, not in subject matter. They are animated by a heroic, triumphant force. The first, "Hail to Tragedy," was inspired by the controversial performance in the demotic of Aeschylus's *Oresteia* in 1903. Its aim was to praise the father of tragedy and to assess the greatness of ancient Greece and that of tragic writings through the ages. At the same time, the poet aimed at inspiring his contemporaries to heroism and greatness.

The second poem, "Ode to Ibsen Upon His Death," was written in 1906, the year of Ibsen's death. It is not only a tribute to Ibsen, who had greatly inspired and influenced Palamas, but is also a reservoir of insights into his own poetic personality and thought.

The last poem of the trilogy, entitled "Garibaldi," is a tribute to the great hero of Italian independence written on the centennial of Garibaldi's birth. Palamas here salutes the ideals of liberty, heroism, and patriotism, and he links the struggles of the Italian hero to his and his country's struggles.

The final poem, "Epilogue," is again, like "To a Woman" at the end of *The Dodecalogue,* of psychological significance. After the flight on the wings of poetry into the heroic realms—the positive, optimistic phase—he returns to the familiar opposite mood: pessimism, weakness, lament.

CHAPTER 5

In the Lyrical Realms—The Self Becomes One with Poetry

THE FIRST decade of the twentieth century is generally considered the culmination of Palamas's creative life. During this period, when Palamas was in his forties, each side of his personality—the lyricist, the visionary, the social revolutionary—found expression in his greatest works: *Life Immovable, The Dodecalogue of the Gypsy,* and *The King's Flute.* A fourth masterpiece, the play *Trisevgeni,* was also written during this decade. In this powerful drama Palamas captured, perhaps more fully than in any other work, the new spirit of Greece that he represented, the beauty and vitality of the demotic tradition and movement. These four works are at once his best and the most representative of his genius.

From 1910, when *The King's Flute* appeared, until the end of his life, Palamas published ten additional collections of poetry, all of which will be discussed in this chapter. One distinct characteristic of these collections is the absence of long compositions, so common in the earlier work. Palamas had actually planned to write several long poems, some of epic dimensions, but was unable to finish any of them. His inability to complete the projected long poems—especially one on Digenes Akritas and one on the revolutionary hero Karaiskakis—was a source of torment to him for many years. Instead, Palamas wrote numerous short poems and became increasingly preoccupied with matters of prosody and form. The thinker, the visionary, the social fighter in Palamas gradually surrendered to the core of his conciousness—the lyricist.

Several factors seem to have been responsible for this change in Palamas, particularly for the abandonment of his plans for the long poems. First of all, he was aging. After 1910 Palamas no longer possessed the strength of youth and his earlier intensity of determination and vision. A second factor is related to changes in the sociopolitical situation in Greece. Following the military revolt of

Goudi in 1909, the brilliant Cretan nationalist Eleutherios Venizelos rose meteorically to assume political power in Greece and eventually lead her through the most turbulent period of her history since the Independence. Venizelos initially rode the tide that manifested itself at the Goudi revolt as a powerful demand for sweeping reforms and reflected the rise of the enlightened bourgeoisie in Greece. To this progressive force that claimed him as its leader, Venizelos added his burning patriotic zeal, his powerful dream for a free and great Greece. The result was what might be expected: extensive reforms, great accomplishments in many areas of national life, accompanied by strife, disunity, and perilous, sometimes catastrophic, adventures.

The initial years of Venizelos's leadership, the most influential on Palamas, were the most positive and most hopeful to the nation. Administrative, agrarian, and educational reform plans were vigorously put into effect by Venizelos, and they immediately gave vitality and national purpose to the people. The progressive inspiration of Palamas's poetry in the past thirty years was now becoming reality, or at least it seemed so, in the new climate of sociopolitical reform. The victorious wars of 1912–13 (Balkan Wars), which expanded Greece vastly, brought fruition to the patriotic aspirations of the younger Palamas. His role as inspirer and leader was now changing into one of reflector and singer of national accomplishments. Individual events and personalities received voices in his poems.

The turn toward the short poem was also affected by a third factor: the state of European art and poetry in the twentieth century, especially after World War I. The fragmented, antiheroic consciousness of Europe could not but touch and affect Palamas, the sensitive receiver of the European experience. His native surge toward the visionary, synthetic poem was eventually abated in the stillness of old age and the fragmenting realities of the times. Only the lyrical impulse remained, the lyrical song.

But if the post-1910 poetry of Palamas was on the wane in terms of intensity and encompassing vision, there was another sense in which his poetry improved. This was on the formal level. As Palamas grew older, his lyrical emotion was distilled into terse, often epigrammatic verses of amazing rhythmical and metric refinement and beauty. His linguistic inventiveness and his rhythmic achievements never ceased to surprise, often amaze, his readers. Even in his deep old age Palamas continued to pulsate with rhythmical-musical throbs. His being gradually became one with his verse; he lived as a poem does. In this lyrical-formal sense Palamas continues to grow. Here there was no decline, only ascent.

I   The Sorrows of the Lagoon and The Satirical Exercises

In 1912 Palamas published *The Sorrows of the Lagoon and The Satirical Exercises* as one volume. *The Satirical Exercises,* series A and B, were written earlier, in 1907 and 1909, and should be looked at first. Both in time and in spirit these satires of Palamas belong to his revolutionary period, to the inner climate and the external conditions that created his Gypsy, attacker and destroyer of everything that is corrupted and false in society. The anger that rages in them is even more vehement than the Gypsy's anger because the satires are not raised to an ideological or symbolic plane; they are themselves a direct link between the poet and the society that causes his wrath.

The satire of Palamas is of the highest order, solemn and biblical in tone and power. There is no trace of humor in these poems, only bitterness and anger. Each poem is an outburst of painful wrath over the stagnation of society and the corruption of the state, a thunderbolt hurled at irresponsible politicians and journalists, as well as the apathetic masses. The intention of the satires is not to ridicule but to devastate. There is something reminiscent of the vengeful anger of Archilochus in them, and the profound anger of the Prophets and of Dante. They are even cast in three-line rhyming stanzas, an imitation of Dante's *terza rima,* except that the four tercets of each poem are followed by a single independent line. Both Archilochus and Dante are mentioned in the satires and their inspiration and influence are acknowledged. The first satire is actually addressed to Archilochus:

> With one hand you grasp the Apollonian lyre,
> with the other the heavens' thunderbolt;
> tempestuous your life and your fate.
>
> Not a single stone remains from the fortress
> of your Work, to sing you out to the passerby.
> Only you, Fame, built a fortress for him, and it stands.
>
> Satire is still quaking
> from the impact of your verse; from the abyss
> your voice deals out joy and death.
>
> Like the marble of your land, Archilochus,
> shining and hard, your glory
> cannot be destroyed by Death.
>
> You stand on Homer's side.

(Works VI, 231)

Most of the poems that follow this introductory one are relentless attacks against each offender in the body politic, against every practice that corrupts and deadens society. Some are exhortations aiming at awakening and action. Rarely a pure lyric, a pose for self-reflection, momentarily changes the tone of urgency and anger. In the satires Palamas uses the rough language of the street and the coffee shop in order to be more effective in his criticism, both in terms of bite and comprehension by a wider public. It is a language that completely defies translation.

In the second series of the satires, written just before the revolt of 1909, Palamas is even more unrestrained as he lashes out at officials, cliques, and the lethargic masses. Beneath the wrath, however, one constantly senses the yearning for regeneration, the hope that a leader will appear to revitalize the decaying nation. When this leader appeared, in the person of Venizelos, Palamas became his ardent supporter and *laudator*. The following satire, the last but one of the second series, evoking both the fate of Oedipus and of fallen Byzantine kings, tragically captures the state of the nation and Palamas's inner state at the time of its composition, just before the arrival of Venizelos:

> He who wanders in the streets
> pulled by the hand of a child,
> he whose bearing reminds you
>
> of heroes and the race of demigods,
> he is the one who once ruled the City,
> her purple-born king.
>
> He is now choked by thorns and thistles,
> his kingdom, throne, power—all torn.
> And, even worse than death's evil shaft,
>
> blindness brought the night to his eyes.
> But he goes on, with the child on his side,
> as though he is to enter his original palaces again.
>
> Who is he? Is he for admiration or pity?
>
> (*Works* VI, 273)

No matter how specific or topical the subject of his poems, Palamas will always lift it above its particular context and make it universal. Even in the satires, the most concretely political poetry he wrote, the timeless elements live side by side with the contemporary and topical. As Palamas himself writes in his *Poetics:*

Although "The Satirical Exercises" . . . start out with the intention of attacking specific persons and practices related to crucial political and social matters, eventually they are drawn toward philosophical formulations and suggestive images.[1]

The philosophical formulations and the suggestive images pertain to the vision of a life to be lived after the destructive rage of the Gypsy and the devastating wrath of the satirist have done their work.

After the long years of struggle in the demotic front and ideological dedication to sociopolitical demands, after his visionary flights and epic journeys, Palamas felt the need to return to the strictly subjective realm. He made this return with *The Sorrows of the Lagoon.* These are poems of pure, almost elemental, emotion; an emotion which is close to sensation, to the original impact of experience on the soul of the youthful poet. The setting is Missolonghi and its lagoon, where Palamas spent most of his childhood and adolescence. This is the primordial territory of all his awakenings.

Now in his early fifties, Palamas returns with his living memories to the days of his youth and sings of the sensations and passions that were his profoundest experiences. He surrenders himself to the spell of these experiences and his imagination becomes intoxicated with them. The poems breathe with the living sensations that inspired them, and at the same time they are hymns to these sensations and to their sources—the lagoon and its surroundings, elements, and people. The poet relives his youth driven by the tragic nostalgia of age. And the pain is intensified by the intuitive awareness of the irretrievability of youth. The tension between emotion and thought, so intensely present in the work of Palamas, becomes a special lament here, as the life of sensation and passion is elevated to the highest order of adoration. The opening poem of *The Sorrows of the Lagoon* dramatizes this tension, and the poems that follow vibrate with the choice:

> My simple, softly-sounding songs
> are seeking you, my Child.
> Whisper them one by one to your new bride-guitar;
> I have tuned them to her tongue, to your liking.
>
> I return to the ruins of my youth,
> the youth I killed without living it.
> I wake the magician Echo and in the echoings
> shades are dancing; sweet reveling begins.

You must give your youth both mind and hands
to build your house sound.
Arete is the Muse of Muses; you must join together
the singer's harp and the citizen's weapons.

(But who knows? Perhaps above the stars,
greater than the summit of Art and the depths of Thought,
is the goddess fire, creator and wrecker,
higher even than Arete, end and beginning of all—Passion.)

("Dedication," *Works* VI, 175)

Most of the poems that follow are hymns to people and localities
around the lagoon and to the unforgettable experiences of youth. The
simple life of fishermen and peasants is praised and envied. Spots in the
Missolonghi area that gave him the unique vision of intense sensation
are described in all their nakedness and beauty. Some of the best poems
are about the girls and women of Missolonghi that ignited in the poet
the first passion for the flesh. But the lagoon itself dominates the whole
collection. The central images come from the lagoon, its shallow and
dirty waters, its death-like calm, its rich and diverse life under the
surface, its strange accumulation of living and dead things. Ultimately,
the lagoon becomes a symbol of Palamas's own soul. In singing its
sorrows, he is singing his own inner torment. Through the lagoon
Palamas has given us one of the most complete pictures of his complex
and tormented consciousness. The profound identification of Palamas
with the lagoon is perfectly expressed in the poem "Delirium."

Lagoon with your debris,
foul-smelling, black, slimy;
you are inside me—abysses, lusts, thorns—
Inside me . . . o my misfortune! o misery!

Who cast me here, an orphaned child?
My mind is all disease. I can't anymore . . .
Where is my father? Where are you, mother?
Pity me, the sinner.

(*Works* VI, 212)

Palamas is again in his kassianic inferno, lost in the dark mass of his
interior lagoon.

Some of the best poems Palamas ever wrote are in *The Sorrows of
the Lagoon.* The return to the inner self—to the lagoon, to youth—
opened channels for communion with the deepest layers of his

consciousness. The lyrical cry is now heard in its fullest, most painful intensity expressing the fundamental discords of his being, the separation from nature, the chasm between passion and fullfilment.

II   *City and Solitude*

In 1912 Palamas published a second book of poems, *City and Solitude*. It is a large collection, containing a vast variety of poems written between 1893 and 1912, many published earlier in magazines. There is nothing new or surprising here that Palamas's other works of this twenty-year period have not shown. These are parallel poems, expressions of the already familiar themes and concerns of the poet. Here under one cover we find the whole poetic world of Palamas, from the most ideological to the most lyrical. Most poems of the collection could not be classified as part of his best work, although they are by no means second-rate poetry. The fact that we are already familiar with their emotions and themes through the earlier collections seems to work against our appreciation of them. This is not true, however, of the best poems of the collection, no matter what their content or date of composition might be.

The title of the collection, *City and Solitude,* suggests a thematic division of the contents and one of the fundamental tensions in Palamas's life and work, the powerful antithetical forces that determine his dedications, the individualistic and the social. ("City" here must be taken in its broadest sense: society, a republic of citizens, a *polis*.) But Palamas's own preface to *City and Solitude* provides the best commentary on this aspect of his poetry:

The poet is inspired by both the collective life around him and the solitary life inside him. External events strike him in his core as if they were his own, while his inner life extends outward and grows in the external world. The poet is, depending on conditions, a cry and an echo. City and Solitude are sometimes Monsters to him, sometimes Muses. . . . At times the poet's word is a bugle call over the City, a heralding sound from the Archangel's mouth; at other times it is a monologue whispered in the Solitude, born in the vitals of the Solitude, something completely unharmonizable and antisocial that stands against the City. But the poet, in order to put in his song the idea of the City, his mother, needs Solitude; and in order to enjoy the dream-nurtured children of Solitude, his mate, he needs the City.[2]

Palamas sees himself with perfect clarity as the poet of the self and the poet of society. And the two always clash and always complement one another, the endless dialectical chain in one of its most concrete manifestations.

Since there is no need to look at the thematic or ideological content of the poems in *City and Solitude,* it might be best to look at a few of its masterpieces as examples of Palamas's lyrical expression. The first, "Rose Fragrance," is perhaps the best known and best loved poem of Palamas:

> This year the rough winter hit me hard;
> it caught me without fire, found me without youth,
> and from hour to hour I waited to crumple,
> a heap on the snow-covered path.
>
> But yesterday, as the smile of March gave me heart
> and I set out to find again the trails of long ago,
> at the first fragrance of a far-off rose
> my eyes filled with tears.
>
> *(Works* V, 431)

In Greek this is a magical poem, exquisitely expressing the poet's emotion, delicately balancing the tragic and sentimental. It is a perfect example of Palamas's restrained lyrical voice, nurtured and uttered in his solitude. In contrast, his "City" poems and most of his hymns are almost always unrestrained and rhetorical, high-sounding and torrential. The difference in emotion and intent determines the specific mode of expression.

Another famous poem of Palamas, "My Greatest Sorrow," is also in *City and Solitude.* The terrible feeling of separation from nature and from the life-giving tangible experiences that he sang in *The Sorrows of the Lagoon* is given one of its fullest expressions in this poem:

> In the supreme hour when death
> will little by little put my light out, one will be
> my greatest sorrow.
> It will not be regret over my useless thoughts, my lost years,
> the anxiety of want, love's sleepless torment—
> a deep thirst in my blood, ancestral curse;
> nor will it be regret over my empty life always pulled
> by the magnetic Muse, or you, my beloved home.
> My greatest sorrow
> will be that I did not live with you,
> o green creation, on mountains, across the seas, in forests;
> that, bent over books, I did not enjoy you
> o Nature—whole life and whole truth!
>
> *(Works* V, 463)

A third masterpiece of Palamas, "The Satyr or the Naked Song," is also in *City and Solitude.* This poem, however, will be looked at in the Conclusion.

When *City and Solitude* was at the printer's, in the fall of 1912, the first Balkan war broke out. The Greeks and other Balkan peoples took up arms again to complete their independence from the Turks. For Palamas, who since 1897 had been lamenting over the listlessness of the country and the fate of the unredeemed Greeks, this was a momentous event. Inspired by the spirit of the new mobilization, the rally of the Balkans for freedom, he wrote twenty-seven poems which he rushed to include in *City and Solitude* under the title "The Land That Armed Itself." In these poems Palamas captures and praises the new surge for freedom and once again returns to this role of poet-patriot.

III   The Altars

In 1915 Palamas published *The Altars,* one of the richest and formally best collections of his poetic work. The poems of this book were written in the interlude between the Balkan Wars and World War I, a relatively calm and positive period in Greek national life. They reflect inner states primarily, a deepening in Palamas's spiritual encountering of existence together with a re-examination of his function as a poet. They are poems of great intellectual power, manifesting also his full technical maturity.

In an intended preface to *The Altars,* not published until 1933 as a part of his *Poetics,* Palamas wrote:

A triple disposition seems to have worked for the arrival of these poems. . . . First an epic tendency to turn into creations of art some outstanding imaginings of my thought—heroes of mine, famous or obscure, named or nameless, of action or of the mind, taken from the tradition of legends or from history. Then a lyrical tendency to confess emotions and inner events which should perhaps have been silenced. And then again a tendency at once epic and lyrical to relate the subjective emotion to the terrible events of these times that entangle in war the small and the mighty, nations and races, fatherlands and societies or the forces that hold over them the unhurled thunderbolt of peril and destruction.[3]

This sounds like the earlier Palamas we are familiar with, and in most respects it is. But there is also something new in *The Altars* which makes it a turning point in his poetic development. There is a solemn (in the liturgical sense), almost hieratic tone in the poems which makes them "altars," both vessels and objects of sacred worship. This heightened tone comes from Palamas's deepened sense of himself as a poet and of the nature and mission of poetry. As he indicates in the same intended preface to *The Altars,* poetry is a unique and autonomous creation whose supreme element is beauty. Whatever else poetry may be or do is secondary, a by-product of its essence, which is beauty. The poet is the creator of the beautiful and his greatest responsibility is to poetry.

In *The Altars* we begin to see the gradual turning of Palamas toward a more pure poetry and a kind of esthetic hermeticism. Some of the factors behind this change were discussed in the opening section of the present chapter. The deviation, however, from the earlier principles, particularly the social responsibility of the poet, is not as radical as it appears. Palamas never abandoned his earlier dedications completely. What we see in his newer poetry, from *The Altars* onward, is a change in emphasis, an intensified rededication to poetry as an independent spiritual-musical creation. This is a natural, perhaps inevitable, development, given the tremendously absorbing verse-making function of a poet like Palamas. The alchemy of verse eventually claimed its creator as an altar-builder of Poetry.

There are too many significant, indeed major, poems in *The Altars* to discuss in any detail within the confines of this chapter. The entire book breathes with the greatness of Palamas, with an overwhelming intensity. Only an indication of the main thrust of the most weighty among them can be given. The opening poem, entitled "Imagination," signals the direction of the poet, the flight that is to follow. It is a prayer and a hymn to the power of poetry, a power that will lift the poet from the abyss of actuality to the "starry realms" of poetic sublimation. It is to imagination that Palamas raises the first altar.

The next poem, "Antiope," is similarly a prayer and hymn to the powerful and beautiful Amazon, daughter of Ares and wife of Theseus, who symbolizes both the beauty of woman and the redeeming strength of health and warlike struggle. This is the first of several poems of *The Altars* dedicated to women who are symbols of beauty and redeeming strength, more tangible counterparts of the imagination. The persistent direction of these, as well as of most poems of the collection, is toward the ideal or the spiritualization of experience. Passion is transformed into ideal or spiritual reality on the wings of poetry; the flesh becomes word, song, art.

A notable exception is the poem "Melenia," whose heroine of the same name is a beautiful and passionate woman, never transcending the throbbing physical actuality of passion. She is a child of the "lagoon" and remains that—the earth-dark, undying lust for life. She is seething, glittering flesh that remains flesh, not a symbol but passion itself, never leaving the burning lagoon of the blood. To her Palamas has written some of his most beautiful verses:

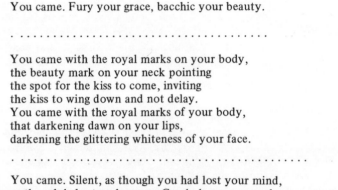

> You came. Fury your grace, bacchic your beauty.
>
> . . . .
>
> You came with the royal marks on your body,
> the beauty mark on your neck pointing
> the spot for the kiss to come, inviting
> the kiss to wing down and not delay.
> You came with the royal marks of your body,
> that darkening dawn on your lips,
> darkening the glittering whiteness of your face.
>
> . . . .
>
> You came. Silent, as though you had lost your mind,
> as though led astray by some Greek daemon or god,
> from a deep merging with a Satyr, reaper of pleasure. . . .
>
> (*Works* VII, 100)

"Melenia" is one of the few poems of Palamas in which passion remains Dionysian. In the vast majority of his poems about women, physical lust is sublimated to the spiritual or celestial realms. As his own words explain:

Erotic passion from being a physiological—libidinal—excitement, little by little, following the development of the mind, becomes mystical passion, becomes the Platonic Phaedrus, the Dantean Beatrice or Antigone the beloved of Shelley in some other life, as he tells us; and so it is with the poet's song: from an outburst of lust, from erotic play for the possession of the enchanting flesh, it gradually comes to embody—by expressing and symbolizing—all great ideas and all the aspirations of the heart which are the pride, the torment and the glory of mankind.[4]

These are the stages, the transformation of the woman in Palamas's poetry, a poetry filled with, one could say dominated by, women. The flesh becomes dream; woman becomes symbol of the Ideal. And so it is in another major poem of *The Altars,* entitled "Women." Here in a gigantic flaring up of his imagination, Palamas raises his greatest altar, the altar of woman. He sings a burning hymn to all the women that excited him in his life, "the pure and the shameless," those that he saw with his eyes and those that lived in literature, in history, in the imagination. And in the song woman becomes again a symbol of the totality of life.

One of the most powerful poems in *The Altars* is "The Airplane," a long and exciting dialogue between a man and a woman. It begins with an epigrammatic assertion by each and then unfolds dramatically into a whole world of intense yearnings, flights of thought and imagination, and realizations about human existence, the whole world of Palamas.

> Man: The more you know, the more fully you love.
> Woman: The more you love, the more you will know.
>
> *(Works* VII, 63)

This is the fundamental conflict in Palamas, the tension beteen wisdom and passion. Man wants to explore, to fly, to fathom the universe. The airplane—"winged ship," "dream vessel"—overwhelms him with excitement for it promises fulfillment to his dream, the hunger for action and knowledge. He flies on the miracle machine only "to meet the thunderbolt" that crushes him back to earth, to his humble hut in order to love what is immediately tangible, to know tragically. And Palamas, as if to console himself, has the woman of the poem cry out to the man: "Winged one, if you fell, your fall was from the heights!" The pattern of Palamas's life: attempts for escape-salvation and glorious defeat, and an inevitable return to the self.

There are other significant poems in *The Altars* which should at least be mentioned here. "Fathers" is a tribute to a chain of inspirers of Palamas, all pioneers in the demotic tradition, from Kornaros, the poet of *Erotokritos,* to Psycharis, the fellow champion of the demotic since the 1880's. Through these "fathers" of the tradition Palamas defines the Neo-Hellenic values and his own relationship to them.

In the section entitled "Unborn Souls" Palamas pays homage to some heroes of his imagination whom he had intended to treat in much longer works. They give us an indication of what the longer works would have been. The poem "Savior" is about Theseus, the hero and savior of Athens, slayer of the Minotaur. Through Theseus Palamas once again finds the opportunity to celebrate the Classical spirit while at the same time he exalts woman and her mysterious power by re-creating Medea in the context of Theseus's life. In "Triumph" he celebrates Lucretius, whose *De Rerum Natura* was for Palamas one of the greatest poems ever written. And through Lucretius he also celebrates the materiality of the world, and the beauty and power of love.

In the fifth section of *The Altars* Palamas manifests himself again briefly as a citizen-poet by writing several poems about contemporary matters. In "An Evening at a Home"[5] he creates a hymn-portrait of Venizelos, his personality as a leader, and the ideals for which he was fighting; essentially these are the ideals of Palamas himself. "Europe," another poem of this section, was written soon after the outbreak of World War I. It is mainly a visionary-philosophical poem in which Palamas speaks again, in a way reminiscent of *The King's Flute,* about war, violence, and necessity under the law of universal change and recurrence. He is here an observer, at best a poet-seer, not an agonized citizen of wartorn Europe.

The last section of *The Altars,* "New Anapaests and Iambs," is a return to the form of Palamas's *Iambs and Anapaests* of 1897, now handled with greater dexterity. These poems contain the familiar feelings and thoughts of Palamas cast in palpitating, brilliant verses. There is a poem-epilogue after the "New Anapaests and Iambs" which clearly manifests the new tone and attitude toward poetry which Palamas introduced with The Altars. Its title, "Liturgy," and its content, reveal the turn toward a heightened, more esoteric poetry, the lifting of the poet's hands toward the "altars" and toward the stars.

IV   *The Last Collections*

In 1919 Palamas published his next collection of poetry, *Poems Out of Season.* As the title indicates, these are poems unrelated to the times, to post-World War I European conciousness. Palamas, well aware of their nature, significantly explains:

As their name shows these are poems that are not related to the conditions around us. I collected them here, putting aside some other cares, as though I wanted to rest for a while, as though I wanted to collect myself, measure my strength and then surge forth again in accordance with a deeper desire. . . . These are poems out of season not because I disdain contemporary things and events, important and impactful as they are. I didn't stretch my hand out to touch events of our days not because I do not care for them, not because I stand untouched by them, but, on the contrary, because I am too concerned.

Yet, the more I think about contemporary things the more I am afraid to touch them.[6]

Palamas, it seems, did not have the strength to cope with the winds that blew his way in the aftermath of the war, the new ideological, psychological, and esthetic currents. As a result, he felt threatened by the new climate and the new poetry. He retreated more and more to his inner self and set out, perhaps involuntarily, to fortify and defend his convictions and poetic practices. But his inability to adjust to the new European reality kept him out of tune with it and crippled his intention "to surge forth again" toward new significant work. Except for a few outstanding instances, he could only repeat himself, although with finer skill. And the longer Palamas found himself out of phase with the times, the further he withdrew toward the deeper regions of the self and toward a purer poetry.

One outstanding feature of *Poems Out of Season* is that they are rhythmical-metrical exercises, one could say acrobatics. Palamas is here showing, almost showing off, his technical virtuosity. And in most cases he is brilliant. Yet he seems to have thought little of the collection:

The songs in *Poems Out of Season* are whistlings of some beloved sounds of mine, accompanying certain deeper preoccupations and intended to aid in the birth of some other songs—not songs out of season but very much of our times, or rather of the times and timeless, songs that I have inside me and constantly long to bring out in the sun.[7]

It is as though he sought, in writing *Poems Out of Season,* a catalytic magic for further more significant achievement.

The introductory poem of the collection reveals the main conflict of Palamas during this period. It is a dialogue between Inspiration and Verse or Form, an outcry of Inspiration for freedom and sovereignty in the creative life and a stern reply by Form and its controlling power to which Inspiration surrenders:

> Inspiration: Ah! Don't choke me, monster!
> I hurt, I hurt.
>
> . . . .
>
> Let me fly in infinite spaces,
> fly everywhere, a wind;
> to become a spirit and enter
> all things, to burn and glitter.

. . . .

> Form: If you desire to fly,
> to be everywhere

. . . .

> You must emprison yourself
> in my tight embrace,the whirlpool.

. . . .

> Inspiration: Hold me, hold me, monster.
> Now I see! You resurrect me.
> In binding me you are
> my fate and my father.

. . . .

> Your violent embrace, a creator;
> your arms, the wings of Pegasos;
> your kisses, the heavens with the stars.
>
> (*Works* VII, 183–84)

This surrendering of the poet to form—metrical verse—gradually leads to his complete absorption by Poetry.

Poems Out of Season includes several compositions of memorable content or lyrical power, especially the longer poems "Eurydice," "The Little Girl on the Grave of Botsaris," "The Cell," and "The Drink and the Glass." "The Cell" is about the book-heaped study in the home of Palamas where he spent endless hours in contemplation and creative toil: "Thirty years here, in this narrow cell./ Here I brought the whole of creation—sea, land, sky" (*Works* VII, 219). "The Drink and the Glass" dramatizes Palamas's oscillation between emphasis on content and emphasis on form, a particularly painful concern during this period. This oscillation is manifested once again as Palamas writes a new dialogue between Inspiration and Form at the conclusion of *Poems Out of Season*. However, there is a reversal here. Inspiration, which stands for content, becomes the dominant force:

> Inspiration: . . . .
> Awake! Hurry!
> I am now the queen,
> you the slave.
> THE TIMES are EPIC.
>
> (*Works* VII, 298)

But this is a dying gasp, a desperate attempt to bring back in his poetry the vitality that comes from involvement with contemporary social reality, so important to the earlier Palamas.

In 1919 Palamas published a second collection of poetry, *The Sonnets*. It contained one hundred and two sonnets, almost all of them written in the same year. Palamas had been fascinated by the sonnet since his youth. Since then he had written many sonnets which were scattered in a number of his works, the best of them in *Life Immovable*. But in 1919, obeying an inner urge, Palamas sought to master the sonnet form, and this time he was completely absorbed by the activity and "delight of sonnet-making." A second need seems to have influenced him in turning to the sonnet, the need to answer his critics who, especially in recent years, had severely attacked him for excessive rhetoricism and other related offenses. By using the sonnet with its inherent qualities of conciseness and wholeness he would show his critics that their charges were unfounded. The result, however, falls short of the expectation. By nature Palamas always felt too much and thought too much, saw too many sides to everything and every question, to be able to contain himself gracefully within the limits of the sonnet. Instead of achieving calm intensity and complete expression of feeling or thought, his sonnets breathe too hard, almost brim over their mold. And in addition, his obsession with detail and fullness of perspective leads him to write a series of sonnets on the same subject, thus losing some of the uniqueness and integrity of a single emotion or thought. There are many memorable sonnets in the collection, and the whole book vibrates with the passionate, all-encompassing lyricism of Palamas, but the overall quality of the poems as sonnets is not fully satisfying.

Palamas knew that a new age was beginning after World War I, and he desperately wanted to be a part of it, to merge with the new spirit of European art and thought. But the weight of his earlier work, his conviction that he was a master in poetry and intellectual leadership, did not allow him to change sufficiently in order to achieve such an integration. His attempts, during the 1920's and early 1930's, to become involved with the contemporary world show primarily his agony resulting from alienation, instead of participation in the life of the times.

The next collection of Palamas's poetry, *The Pentasyllabics and The Passionate Whispers,* appeared in 1925. Almost the entire content of the book is older work ("Pentasyllabics:" Series A, 1910, Series B, 1915–17; "Passionate Whispers:" Series A, 1910–11, Series B, 1920;

only two poems, in the group entitled "The Wolves," were written after 1920). In a long, highly introspective Prologue to the collection, written in 1925, Palamas again takes stock of himself, to understand and overcome his artistic crisis. The intention is to clarify, fortify, and defend himself. Some excerpts from this significant Prologue will help further to identify the nature of his crisis.

The poems in *The Pentasyllabics and The Passionate Whispers* bring us from the clear and airy heights, from calm emotional intensity, to the burning sub strata of hidden torment. . . .[8]

The majority of them, the most characteristic of the book, are offsprings of an uneasiness of mind, of a tiredness and a boredom; they appear with a terribly pale face and lips from which the smile seems to have gone permanently. Only their form makes them worth while. . . .[9]

I live in the pre-war times. Not because the devastating waves of the post-war revolutions in all areas of knowledge do not lash me. . . . But I feel that I cannot walk steadily on the quake-struck, quake-cracked territories. . . . Many events are impactful but nothing binds me with the contemporary things.[10]

In terms of technical achievement the collection is strong, if not consistently outstanding. Some poems, especially in the second series of *The Passionate Whispers,* are memorable as lyrical expressions. But the most significant poems are in the concluding section where Palamas is able to become deeply involved again with the fate of contemporary Greece, particularly in the devastating events of 1922. The title poem of this section, "The Wolves," and "The Song of the Refugees" that follows it are heartrending responses to the catastrophic defeat of the Greeks in Asia Minor, which was also the end of the Great Idea, and to the suffering that it caused to the defeated and homeless. Here the poet-patriot, the consciousness of his people, expresses his pain, and once again enlists himself in the service of Greece as her consoler, counselor, and regenerator.

In 1928 a new collection of poetry, *Verses Mild and Harsh* appeared in Chicago, published by the Plato Hellenic Collegiate Club. It is a large collection, containing a great variety of poems written over a vast period of time, going as far back as 1885. In terms of quality it is a very uneven book. Some of Palamas's best poems are included along with some that are very poor. But in its entirety it is one of the richest and strongest of his works. As A. Karandonis writes:

Putting aside its purely poetic value, *Verses Mild and Harsh* is the most diverse and the richest book of Palamas, both in themes and sources of inspiration, a book which, in spite of its unevennes, gives us a clear picture of his poetics and illuminates the backstage workings of his art. One is dazzled by the flexibility and the unconquerable soaring of his imagination, the exceptional power of his unique poetic mechanism that has the ability to turn into poetry not only the great philosophical and lyrical themes but even the mundane, ordinary moments of our lives.[11]

Verses Mild and Harsh is the last book of Palamas that vibrates with his full power. Even the titles of some of its sections excite the reader's imagination: "Moments and Rhymes," "Lyrical Rhythms," "Pulses and Rhythms," "Sobbings and Angers," "Alma Venus." Only a few of its most important poems, however, can be touched upon here.

"Moments and Rhymes" contains twenty-six well-wrought rhyming poems, all twelve lines long. They can be grouped with the best poems of Palamas, especially three of them, numbers 14, 19, and 22. "Sobbings and Angers" includes two of Palamas's masterpieces: "All-Souls Sabbath" and "Workers." In "Alma Venus" we find the most beautiful erotic poems of Palamas: "The Swan to Leda" and "Hymn to Passion." The latter is a major poem. "Letters and Dedications" contains the exquisite lyric "Vanna," a fine tribute to the poet "Lambros Porphyras" and another to "Emerson, Poe and Whitman." In "Holidays," the last section of the book, we find another masterpiece. "Thomas," in which Palamas bares his heart, tormented by philosophical doubt and religious anxiety.

In the following year (1929) Palamas published *The Cycle of Quatrains,* another example of his complete absorption by a particular verse form, and an attempt to master it to the fullest. Palamas is now seventy years old and ailing. His restriction to the short poem is clearly a physical necessity, whatever the other, psychological or lyrical, reasons may be. And, significantly, all the poems that he wrote from this time until his death are quatrains.[12] The consequence of having to confine himself to the terse expression is keenly discussed by E. Hournouzios:

Wherever Palamas is forced to confine himself to the short poem he becomes, perhaps without knowing it, gnomic or aphoristic. But this kind of poetry is more didactic than lyrical. And the songs of *The Cycle of Quatrains,* when they succeed in escaping the gnomic or aphoristic dryness, give the impression of lyrical meditation rather than of lyrical gushing. Only a few of the quatrains enclose a miniature lyrical symphony.[13]

Yet there are strength and brilliance here. In the balancing of the gnomic and the lyrical, Palamas achieves a fine distillation of his wisdom and his humanistic emotions. He embraces what is external to him, especially the tangible suffering man, with tenderness and understanding. And the reader feels here a profound, almost mystical, identification of the self with the things of the world.

In 1930 Palamas published *Music Twice Tuned,* a collection of translations of his favorite European poets, which will be discussed in the next chapter. In the following year he published a book of his own poetry, *Wanderings and Salutations.* As a lyrical work it is like a stream next to the robust rivers of his best lyrical creations. Its poems are almost exclusively preoccupied with the self, the poet, and his art. It is as though they were written to illustrate Palamas's lyrical mechanisms, to illuminate his personality and its manifestations as poetry. A. Karandonis calls it "one of the most important lyrical epilogues of Palamas."[14] But it is more like a recapitulating conclusion of a book than the finale of a symphony.

In 1935 Palamas published the last collection of poetry before his death. *The Nights of Phemios,* two hundred and sixty-four quatrains. It is his last desperate attempt to remain on the ramparts of poetry. Since around 1930 he has been ill and slowly losing his strength. He was also losing the use of his right hand, his writing hand, which was gradually becoming paralyzed. The poems of *The Nights of Phemios* were written at the beginning of his long twilight; it was the last luminous burst of his imagination, a song raised against the coming night.

I. M. Panayotopoulos has written brilliantly about this tragic period of Palamas's life:

The Nights of Phemios was written in 1931 and 1932. The poet is beyond his seventieth year and feels his strength gradually diminishing. The chair of old age—his physical "life immovable"—becomes his fate. Only the eyes of his soul are left to him. His body's eyes are tired, their flame a trembling spark; his unique thick eyebrows become shields that cloud the sky. Green creation speaks less and less inside him. The song is his only life—his whole, unbroken, undying being. It is his passing through life and his immortality. And he breathes his song—

impoverished, narrow, patient song—until his last moment. It is the only consolation in his total isolation.[15]

Yet, in spite of the dying flame, the quatrains of *The Nights of Phemios* glitter; they pulsate with the light of the soul. The poet identifies himself with the Homeric minstrel and sings—beyond the turbulence of passions and events, above his former epico-lyric ferment—pure songs that are eternal in their tranquil beauty. Palamas becomes one with his song.

CHAPTER 6

Palamas and World Literature

ONE OF the most illuminating ways of approaching the work of Palamas is to examine it in relation to the Western European heritage; to single out the writers he admired most deeply and discover their influences on his work. During his long and extremely active intellectual life, Palamas came in contact with a vast literary and philosophical tradition, and assimilated a great variety of ideas. The protean quality of his work is primarily the result of rich and diverse influences. Since his youth Palamas was an inspired student of Classical literatures, and their effect on his development was profound. Similarly, he was influenced by oriental writings and the Bible. But the leading European minds of the nineteenth century, particularly those of the last half, had the greatest impact on his personality. And it was through French literature and criticism that he was able to reach literatures otherwise inaccessible to him.

I Palamas and Goethe

The Olympian personality of Goethe was for Palamas a source of constant inspiration. Before Solomos awakened him to the beauty of language and poetry, and before his European contemporaries inspired him with their dramatic conceptions of society and history, Goethe gave him the first stimulus toward poetic sublimation. For Palamas, Goethe's work was the perfect example of Classical unity which he struggled to attain all his life. The "great harmonizer," as he calls Goethe, taught him to seek the unity of the particular and the universal:

Our being is not yet filled with the wisdom of Goethe. There is no doubt that literature begins with the self, expresses the self, and is nothing without the self; but the most significant literary art is that which, without leaving the self isolated, is able to embrace, like the light, the entire external world.[1]

This principle guides Palamas's poetry both when he deals with ideals and with actual social problems. And in the following lines about Goethe many of Palamas's own ideals are again reflected:

Among the towering figures of the century—mad, morbid and convulsive because of their own greatness—stands the tranquil Olympian, strong and unshakable. He who came to know and shape in himself every ideal and all wisdom; who lived the life of all that is passed, resurrected the civilizations of all peoples, and became the philosopher of all ideas and the singer of every emotion.[2]

This universality of Goethe, who is "everything in a high degree," was the sun which illuminated Palamas's life and creative action. In his critical works and his introductions, he constantly quotes Goethe, the teacher and guide of his thought. Goethe's maxim that those who have art and science have religion became an important principle in Palamas's life and a central theme in his work. And Goethe's cry, "Away from all that is dead; love what is living!" shaped one of Palamas's most fundamental attitudes toward his environment.

II *Palamas and the Romantics*

Palamas was profoundly influenced by Romantic poets whose temperaments and world views were radically different from those of Goethe. This is in agreement with his strong disapproval of the one-sidedness in many of the contemporary poets who followed exclusively either the Byronic model or the Classical side of Goethe. He observes that Goethe and Byron admired each other and adds: "The greatness of the Goethean poet lies in his divine tranquillity; the power of the Byronic springs from his satanic anger. The first has the weakness of coolness, the second that of sliding to the rhetorical."[3] In Palamas these two poetic temperaments are combined, and in his poetry he attempts consciously to avoid the extremes inherent in them. In Byron, Palamas found the revolutionary spirit and the power of extreme individualism which he needed in his own struggles. The association of Byron with the Greek War of Independence and with Missolonghi, where Palamas lived as a child, kindled the love of the young Palamas for the Romantic poet. "The poetry of Byron is great," he writes, "but Byron the man is, in a sense, greater than his poetry." [4] And as with Palamas, so with Greece; the heroic life of Byron was a source of inspiration for freedom and action.

Victor Hugo is another poet who inspired Palamas with his Romantic fire. Hugo, like Byron, was actively concerned with the fate of contemporary Greece, and this concern brought Palamas and other Greek writers even closer to him and to the Romantic spirit in general. In an essay entitled "Victor Hugo and Greece," Palamas shows Hugo's relation to Greece and at the same time the relation of the Romantic and the Classical world views. The poet who did not seek perfection but the "immensity of things" achieved harmony in the sublimity of his expression and may be considered Classical in the sense that he achieved an expression of the whole. "The secret of Hugo's art lies precisely in his total expression, the ' word of the Highest,' as he calls it. So many others before and after him have known this 'word' incompletely; he expressed it entire."[5] In the love of Hugo for Greece—Classical and eternal Greece—Palamas sees the classical side of romanticism and points to truth and beauty as the common ideals of Classicism and Romanticism. Hugo's poetic-cultural movement from the Greece of Byron's grave to that of Sophocles ("Le Chant du Sophocle a Salamis"), Palamas compares with the time movement from the present to the distant origins of Romanticism. "The sources of Romanticism," he writes, "are buried in the depths of the past."[6] This conception is part of Palamas's attempt to relate the Classical and Romantic views of life. Writing about Hugo still, Palamas defines poetry as "the Logos that gives flesh to the immaterial things and makes the worldly immaterial; the Logos that gives form to the idea and measureless sublimity to form. . . . Of such a function of poetry the careful student of Hugo becomes profoundly aware."[7] Hugo is for Palamas both the *patridolatre* (lover of country) and the cosmopolitan poet who said "a poet is a world enclosed in a man," and "I love all the suns and all the countries." And Palamas himself expressed and lived this ideal: "I am a citizen of the world and the earth is my fatherland" *(Poems Out of Season)* And

> I am a man; nothing that is human is strange to me
> and I may become familiar with everything.
> And since my fatherland is a world,
> the world too is a fatherland.
>
> *(Altars*—"The Airplane")

But above all Palamas saw Hugo as a giant fighting for the popular language and the democratic ideals. And the moral support of this fighter who suffered for his people and his ideas was, for Palamas, the demotic revolutionary, a powerful force of inspiration. Byron and

Hugo influenced Palamas more significantly in his early, revolutionary period. The individualism of the first, and the universality and humanism of the second, left permanent marks on his personality.

III *Palamas and the Parnassians*

In the Parnassian poets Palamas found the kind of thought and poetry which satisfied the Classical side of his temperament. From them, and particularly from Leconte de Lisle, he took the idea of a pure poetry which demands "the veneration of art, the disdain of easy success." It was Leconte de Lisle's constant preoccupation with the demands of form that primarily interested Palamas. Like the strict Parnassian master, he also sought the perfection of form and labored painstakingly to achieve it. "Perfect poetry," he writes, "exists only in verses of perfect workmanship."

The depth and breadth of Leconte de Lisle's thought were also of importance for the "thoughtful singer" Palamas. The epic imagination of Leconte de Lisle surveyed the historical past of humanity and re-created rhythmically the old forms of life and thought. Palamas, similarly, plunged into the history and lore of many peoples in order to draw material for his poetry. Palamas, however, like Hugo, gave a modern meaning to past situations and forms of life, unlike Leconte de Lisle, who remained entirely in the historical context of his visions. Therefore, it was Leconte de Lisle's formal and philosophical side that influenced Palamas; his extreme intellectual objectivity could not significantly affect the subjective Palamas. To Flaubert's doctrine of form and to the impersonality of art, Palamas reacted in a similar negative manner.

Among the Parnassians, Sully Prudhomme is the poet who is closest to Palamas's poetic temperament. In him Palamas saw a reflection of himself, particularly in the late Prudhomme who, like Anatole France, broke away from the Parnassians and concerned himself with the moral and philosophical problems of his time. The philosophical *aspiration* of Prudhomme, as contrasted to Leconte de Lisle's aim for *représentation,* is one of the chief strains in Palamas's work. He writes about Prudhomme:

He thinks highly of the purpose of his art. The poet, he holds, must present in his verse the highest and the deepest questions of life. He is not, as they have called him, a "singer of nature" but a singer of the human spirit. He does not only paint man's great sentiments but above all he analyzes the minute quivers of the emotions.[8]

In these lines Palamas reveals himself and his affinity with Prudhomme. But it is in the symbolism of the two poets that their similarity is most clearly shown. Their symbols are mainly ornamental images with a definite mythological or natural content without the abstract autonomy, the musical suggestiveness, and the penetrating sharpness of the Baudelairian symbol. Palamas was also influenced by several other representatives of the diverse and constantly changing Parnassian group, particularly Gautier, Hérédia, Baudelaire, Ménard, and Anatole France. Their influence, however, was again through their characteristic insistence on formal perfection.

IV   *Symbolists and Other French Poets*

Palamas was a thorough student of the French Symbolist poets and the leading figure in introducing Symbolism to Greece. He did not, however, respond to their theories as strongly as he did to the Parnassian ideas. This is true of the response of Greek poets in general; Symbolism never became truly native to Greece because of the lack of affinity between the Greek spiritual climate and the Symbolist mood. The brilliance and transparency of the Greek landscape are qualities which do not favor the Symbolist mood of the closed space and the exotic spiritual voyages. The world of Greece favors a plastic poetry rather than a musical one, musical in the Symbolist sense. The intense sunlight and the harmonious land and seascapes keep man a captive to the immediate and do not spur him to search for the exotic regions of the spirit. The symbol of Palamas is drawn from his plastic environment; it is an auxiliary force in his poetry, never an end in itself, like the symbol of Baudelaire. Therefore, the chief influence of Symbolism on Palamas and on his contemporary poets in general was again one for greater respect of form and of the spiritual significance of art. Another influence of the Symbolists on Palamas was effected through their exaltation of the word.

In the Introduction to his *Music Twice Tuned,* a volume of translations, Palamas gives a full account of his understanding of the poets whom he translated and his affinities with them—"a fragment of his own lyrical self." Among the outstanding French poets, or poets writing in French, who appear in the collection are Hugo, Gautier, Leconte de Lisle, Baudelaire, Verlaine, Moréas, Verhaeren, and Valéry. Mistral, Heine, Carducci, D'Annunzio, and Pascoli are also included in this attempt at "reharmonizing."

Baudelaire moves Palamas with "the heavy fragrance that the

'flowers of evil' spread in the damned garden of the soul" and with the perfect harmony of his verses. In Baudelaire, Palamas discovers counterparts of his own consciousness, particularly the strained coexistence of antithetical tendencies. Baudelaire, like himself, is both a materialist and a spiritualist, alternately sinking in the swamps of flesh and aspiring for a sort of "thrones and dominations" in the Idea.

In Valéry, Palamas admires the philosophical depth and the richness of thought, but again he does not abandon himself to the extremes of Symbolist or neo-Symbolist techniques.

Reading the prose studies of Valéry, which are the most illuminating guides to his poetry, I felt for the first time how keenly and wisely he introduces us to its labyrinths with the examples of Leonardo da Vinci, and a hidden joy shook me. And again I saw very clearly that the volcano of the heart does not suffice for the delight of creation without the aid of the light that gleams in the temple of the mind.[9]

Palamas here shows his understanding and admiration for the difficult Neo-Symbolist poet and at the same time reveals his own passion for unity of thought and emotion.

Although there are some similarities in the work and thought of Palamas and Mallarmé, the two poets are basically very different. Mallarmé's idea of absolute and pure-of-all-passion poetry is strictly in opposition to the passionate and subjective nature of Palamas. And Mallarmé's metaphysical conception of a poetry which attempts to give an "Orphic explanation of the Earth" is, in essence, much different from Palamas's pantheistic view of poetry. Palamas could not breathe freely in the narrow confines of Mallarmé's pure verse.

Claudel is one of the outstanding French poets toward whom Palamas felt a strong antipathy, an antipathy that often took the form of a polemic. The theological preoccupation of Claudel, as well as that of Jammes and Viélé-Griffin, is what Palamas disliked in his poetry.

I feel the greatness of Claudel and I see his grandeur, but I always stand far from him. . . . His poetry, with its fluid language, seems to be all fire emerging from the bowels of the earth. But somehow it stands, without setting foot on the earth, in the black and white clouds of a fierce Catholicism which reminds one of a Christ with a sword rather than one with a cross. It is the poetry that throws to the dung with the dogs some *infamous* men, as he calls them, and who are Voltaire, Renan, Hugo.[10]

The mystical faith that animates Claudel's poetry is something distant to the skeptical, pantheistic Palamas.

Palamas speaks with particular enthusiasm about Frédéric Mistral, whose poetry in the modern Provençal idiom he passionately admired. The two poets have many common characteristics of personality and poetics and, in addition, filled similar positions with regard to their respective poetic traditions. Mistral's contribution toward the' enrichment of the Provençal tongue parallels Palamas's enrichment of the demotic. Both poets share a peculiar Classic-Romantic temperament, which is often found in the Greco-Latin peoples of the Mediterranean coast. Camus the "pagan" is a striking recent example of this temperament. Palamas translated Mistral's "Mireio" and several other poems and considered him one of the leading poets of the age.

Anatole France is a writer whom Palamas studied with devotion. He was primarily inspired by the early pagan and Classical works of France like *Les Noces corinthiennes* and *Thaïs*. The simultaneous interest of Palamas in the Christian and Classical cultures was enkindled by France's similar pursuits. Palamas was particularly fascinated by Anatole France's ability to blend many diverse elements of thought and color.

Among Palamas's contemporaries, the Belgian poet Emile Verhaeren can best be compared with him. In their poetry one experiences the same uncontrollable passion which springs from their vision of modern man in a world dominated by science. Both were influenced by Renan's and Guyau's philosophical conceptions of science, and their enthusiasm for the modern age created a lyricism resonating with images from the technological realm long before the arrival of the futurists. They are both pantheists, lovers of nature, and visionaries of future superior men. Their humanism and optimism spring from a vision of the future and from the admiration of human intelligence. Both poets developed free verse to a high order of beauty and were above all lyrical poets. But their most striking similarity is that, while intensely interested in the external world, they are dramatic poets of the interior—lyricists of the tormented self. As one critic of Verhaeren writes: "All the events and adventures of his life are of a psychological—an inner—order; all the defeats and victories are in his soul."[11] The same is true of Palamas. In this subjective mold both poets expressed the aspirations of our age and gave an epic grandeur to many elements of modern life. Amy Lowell has said of Verhaeren that "he has made poetry realize the modern world" and that "he made us understand that art and science are never at variance."[12] Palamas's contribution in this area is similar, and perhaps equal to Verhaeren's.

There is a marked similarity between Palamas and the poets of *l'Ecole romane* and particularly its founder, the Greek-born Jean Moréas. The Classical compositions of Moréas, Maurras, and Henri de Régnier reflect strongly the manner and attitude of Palamas in his *Iambs and Anapaests*. Moréas had met Palamas in Athens in 1897 and expressed his overwhelming admiration for the *Iambs and Anapaests*. It is no exaggeration to say that Moréas's *Stances* were composed under the strong influence of Palamas. The French critic Roger Milliex considers this influence on Moréas a significant contribution of Palamas to French poetry.[13]

V *The Ethical and Social Masters*

Palamas places Tolstoi, Ibsen, and Nietzsche above all the European writers of the last half of the nineteenth century. The great differences in the world views of these "idol breakers," as he calls them, do not stop Palamas from considering them prophets of one world toward which humanity is evolving. In Tolstoi, Palamas sees the moral rebel who brings a new "gospel" to mankind. What concerns him most in the work of Tolstoi is the problem of harmonizing individual and social morality. Then, in Palamas's love for the Greek peasants and the demotic tradition, one sees elements of Tolstoi's "populism." Tolstoi's ideas of the human soul and its values also had a strong influence on Palamas. "The writings of Tolstoi make us think every moment about the true value of life and above all about what is most significant according to the measure of the soul," he writes.[14] He considers Tolstoi a poet of the natural and the moral man who moves toward completeness through his moral growth.

Ibsen was for Palamas the greatest hero of social reform and the finest example of the modern social mind. The revolutionary ideas of Ibsen are found in many works of Palamas, particularly in his play *Trisevgeni* and in *The Dodecalogue of the Gypsy*. The Gypsy and Ibsen's Brand grew out of a similar moral crisis, out of spiritual bondage and a sense of cultural decay, and both seek freedom and spiritual growth. The Gypsy, like Brand, is a torch which endeavors to fire the souls of his fellow tribesmen. The Gypsy's search for self-knowledge is also reminiscent of Peer Gynt's search for his soul. Finally, one of the most striking qualities of Palamas is that which he himself attributed to Ibsen: "a double-faced Janus, now social and now individualist."[15]

In Nietzsche's philosophy Palamas found many ideas which helped him to solve his psychological and artistic problems. Constantly living the antagonisms of the Apollonian and Dionysian forces, of Classical Hellenism and Christianity, Palamas found in Nietzsche's writings ideas which inspired him to seek their understanding. Like Nietzsche, Palamas criticized his culture and worked for its regeneration. Nietzsche's ideas of asceticism and of the relationship of the individual to the mass are clearly echoed in *The Dodecalogue;* the Gypsy as a moral and cultural *agonistes* is a brother of Zarathustra. The Gypsy's love of the earth and the forests and his hatred of the cities are reminiscent of Zarathustra's words: "I love the forest. It is bad to live in the cities: there, there are too many of the lustful."[16] And the feelings of Gypsy as he breaks away from society are not without a Zarathustrian touch. A close comparison of the Gypsy and Zarathustra would reveal numerous affinities in mood and spirit.

VI *Critics and Men of Science*

Palamas studied French criticism with the same passion that he read French poetry. Renan, Taine, Sainte-Beuve, Amiel, Flaubert, and Brunetière were among the critics who contributed decisively in the shaping of his thought. Among these, Taine and Renan were most influential. Taine's theories of milieu and the interdependence of art and society are constantly recurring in the works of Palamas. According to Taine, the purpose of the literary artist is moral and his function clearly social. In many ways Palamas's work is a fulfillment of social demands, and his art is to a significant degree a product of his milieu and the demands of his "race" and "time." Taine's scientific positivism links him—and Palamas—with Renan and Herbert Spencer. With Renan, Palamas shares an enthusiasm for science and a belief in the ultimate triumph of man's intellect. For him Renan presents, like the ancient Greeks, a rational order in which universal ideas stand above everything else. Discussing Renan, Palamas characteristically writes: "Man the individual is nothing; humanity is everything."[17] This surprising statement by Palamas the individualist may be considered an explosion of momentary enthusiasm showing the sweeping influence of Renan.

In the following contrast of Taine and Amiel, Palamas demonstrates his ability to assimilate and harmonize opposing views and ideas:

Taine and Amiel: two great thinkers of entirely opposing intellectual natures. I admire the first, who is positive and adamant, because he uncovers for me one truth. . . . But how I love the other, the protean . . . who is all images and instability! . . . In the mirror that he presents I see something like one of my many selves. . . . What moves me more than anything else in Taine is not his philosophy, but the poetry through which he expresses his philosophy.[18]

During his lifetime Palamas, who was as protean in his criticism as in his poetry, presented several antithetical views of art, each dynamic and creative but not complete in itself. In his later years he returned to an early conception of the autonomy of poetry. But his social concerns of the middle period proved extremely fertile; they were responsible for some of his greatest work.

Palamas understood the critical demands of his time and wrote with an acute awareness of those demands. "Our age," he writes, "is one of the greatest in human history and one of the most critical."[19] His turn to the contemporary leaders of thought manifests his critical preoccupation and strengthens his own criticism. The theories of Freud, for example, became a strong weapon in Palamas's interpretation of art, particularly of his own. In the realm of criticism he exhibits a diverse eclecticism which agrees with the complexity of his personality and the varying demands of creation. What remains constant in Palamas is not his poetics but his psychological relation to poetry. Poetry is the crown of life and the "savior" of the poet. The mystic estheticism of his last period came as a climactic unity of the poet with his art.

VII *English, American, and German Writers*

Through the writings of Taine, Palamas came in contact with English literature. He became particularly familiar with the works of Shakespeare, Keats, Shelley, Coleridge, Carlyle, Tennyson, and Swinburne; and each of these writers inspired him and contributed ideas for his work.

Among American writers Palamas knew Poe, Whitman, and Emerson best. From Poe, through Baudelaire, he received an influential lesson for lucid workmanship in poetry. Whitman's unrestrained streams of emotion and language and his hymns to man, nature, and democracy were rich sources of inspiration for Palamas. In a poem dedicated to this "godlike trinity" Palamas calls Whitman "a Niagara striking the Lyre;"[20] and elsewhere he compares Whitman with the rivers and forests of America and praises his ability "to receive every sensation directly from nature without an interpreting medium."[21] Emerson's essays on nature, man, and art were treasures of wisdom for Palamas.

After Goethe, Schiller, and Heine, the German lyric poets best known to Palamas were George and Rilke. In George's poetry Palamas admired the Classical control, the aristocratic view of art, and the cosmopolitan ideas. During the last years of his life, Palamas found in Rilke the mystical force and the musical symbolism which characterized his own esthetic mysticism in the depths of his ascetic solitude. Palamas, the man who once lived with the positivism and the individualistic faith of the nineteenth century, withdrew, during the last period of his life, into the mystical spheres of art and came to intimate communion with Rilke, the man who lived and expressed the death and aloneness of man in "our age which does not have any temples." Sikelianos has spoken of the profound effect of *Die Aufzeichnungen des Malte Laurids Brigge* on Palamas.[22] As Palamas approached the end of his life, the poet of solitude, God and Death became his greatest spiritual companion.

VIII *Palamas's Place in World Literature*

Many other writers, among whom are D'Annunzio, Pascoli, Unamuno, Hardy, and William James, stimulated Palamas's thought. All contributed to the creation of his protean art. The brief treatment of influences in this chapter is by no means complete. The emphasis, as far as influence of ideas is concerned, has been placed on non-Greek tradition. In the Byzantine writings and in the rich folk tradition he found an inexhaustible treasure of language and prosody which he used and perfected. No other Greek writer surpasses Palamas in his ability to draw creatively from the virgin regions of Greek language and life.

From the world outside Greece Palamas needed ideas in order to link Greece with Europe and the entire world and so achieve her modernization, backward as she was after the long slavery. This task of uniting Greece with the rest of the world through literature makes Palamas important from the point of view of world and comparative literature. Palamas followed Goethe's idea of *Weltliteratur* throughout his life. He saw the literatures of the world as one whole and plunged into them with an acute awareness of their unbroken continuity and unity. He understood the need of modern times for universal ideas, and his work was an attempt to show the linking forces of humanity as they are manifested in literature. "The works of imagination in all times, and perhaps more in our age of immense development of communications, have been nurtured in a sense by mutual borrowings,"[23] he wrote in 1898, reflecting upon the contemporary literary movements and influences. His own poetic synthesis of many diverse ideas which influenced him shows the unity and interdependence of a number of distinct literary streams. In his voluminous critical writings, literary traditions and writers are always presented in terms of their relations to each other, thus forming a continuous comparative study. In his criticism he constantly employs the method of comparison and contrast. "I love, I compare, I judge, I establish. These are the stages of criticism," he writes.[24] This statement sketches his entire critical function. With the word "love" he expresses not only the qualitative function of literary appreciation but also a quantitative embracing of works from all literatures. The word "compare" shows his passion for relating each literary work to the whole production of the human mind. Then comes the evaluation, and finally the placement of the work in the body of world literature.

As Palamas's intellectual and spiritual world grew, he came to see himself and his work not only as part of the Greek tradition but also as a part of the European and the world community. This enabled him to grasp the meaning of one humanity and one history which led him to an idealistic panhumanism akin to Romain Rolland's. "The literary history of a people is a part of the immense literary body of the great European civilization, regardless of all its distinct temperamental and racial characteristics,"[25] he writes, and he means world civilization, though in the context he writes European. Through a wide view of literature and all art, a unity of the world can be created. This is the essence of Palamas's universalism.

CHAPTER 7

Conclusion

IN THE FINAL years of his life, although he was drained of physical and mental strength, Palamas attempted to write a few more poems. All his attempts were faint echoings of what he once had been. When the war came, he was almost lifeless. Even so, he made a desperate effort to give his last report to Greece on the eve of her new tragedy. In a momentary flickering of strength and inspiration Palamas wrote (in March, 1941) a powerful patriotic poem, "Victory," a hymn to Greece and to freedom, his very last poem. Death came on February 27, 1943, when Greece was going through the most terrible days of occupation, when famine, executions and deportation to concentration camps were killing her people by the thousands. The news of his death spread like lightning across Athens and the whole country. The Greek people were stunned but also quickened. The next day hundreds of thousands walked in tense silense behind the body of Palamas, on the way to his grave. And the last tribute to their Father and spiritual leader was overwhelming. As his coffin was lowered into the grave, Angelos Sikelianos, the greatest living poet after Palamas, improvised and recited a great poem to Palamas:

> Trumpets, resound! . . . Church bells thunder!
> Shake the whole body of our land. . . .
> All of Greece rests on this coffin!
> The name "Palamas" reverberates across the world.
>
> . . . .
>
> Unfold the terrible banners of liberty!

And then, as if the spirit of Palamas had seized the immense crowd around the grave, there was a burst. The people began singing the Greek national anthem—Solomos's *Hymn to Liberty*—in complete defiance of the conquerors who had surrounded the cemetery with tanks and armored cars. Even in death Palamas could merge his being with the fate of Greece—his life a struggle for her renaissance, his death an inspiration for her freedom.

It is difficult to think of a poet as completely dedicated to poetry and a man as completely absorbed by Hellenism as Palamas was. His life and his work were dominated by two great passions, poetry and Hellenism, whose intensity and range are difficult to imagine as humanly possible. As a poet he was the ever-wakeful, ever-creating singer of life, a rhapsode and a hierophant of Verse. As a Greek and a Hellenist he was the unifier of an immense tradition and the fulfiller of a cultural need that had been unfulfilled for two thousand years. As George Seferis puts it:

Behind the door that Palamas endeavors to open are crowded centuries of events, persons, emotions, legends, religions, tales, triumphs and calamities—all in agony, awaiting the *logos,* the living language, that would give them flesh and the light of the sun.[1]

Profoundly aware of his historical mission, Palamas opened this door and channeled the flooding life that surged forth through it.

As a poet he moved across the entire spectrum of poetic function, from bard and seer to nightingale; his concerns ranged from the social and philosophical to the purely musical or purely formal. As A. Karandonis writes:

The poetry of Palamas has something difficult to capture, something dizzying in it. One moment he is in heaven, the next moment on the earth. . . . Sometimes he appears in rags, losing himself democratically and humbly among the masses, at other times he preaches from the pulpit of emperors and bishops, immersed in purple. He worships Athena and Virgin Mary with the same ideological and aesthetic passion, one moment in Hagia Sophia the next on the Acropolis. . . . Sometimes we find him in Constantinople, sometimes in Missolonghi. He is everywhere—Attic, Byzantine, plethoric, violent, hysterical, revolutionary, cyclical, changeable, militant and tender, hymnic and satirical, smiling and wrathful, optimistic and pessimistic, arrogant and humble. . . . He felt deeply and believed mystically in the omnipotence of the word . . . in the salvation that comes from the perfect beauty of art.[2]

Palamas was, above all, a man of passion and a lyrical poet. And it seems fitting to conclude this book on Palamas with an attempt to show the lyrical intensity and beauty of his poetry. The poem that follows is one of the finest examples of his lyrical genius. In it the passion of the flesh and the passion of the intellect—the Dionysian and Apollonian forces—breathe in their fullest intensity and find perfect balance; the lagoon of the subjective self and the Attic light of objective reality—the Idea—meet and blend harmoniously. It is "The Satyr or the Naked Song" of *City and Solitude:*

. . . .

All around us a naked world.
All things are naked here:
plains, mountains, skies.
The day limpid and pure;
creation is transparent,
her deep palaces wide open.
Eyes, fill yourselves with light,
guitars, with rhythm!

Here trees are stains,
rare and out of place.
The world is unmixed wine;
nakedness is queen.
Here the shade is a dream;
a golden smile
still dawns here,
even on the lips of misty night.

Nature is bare-breasted here,
lusting without shame;
the barren rock is a star,
the body a flame.
Your divine nakedness,
o noble Attica, scatters
rubies and golden things,
pearls and silvery things.

Here the body is magical,
the flesh is deified;
virginity is Artemis,
Hermes is desire.
And every hour
Aphrodite rises
to fill the world—
a miracle to sea creatures.

—Strip yourself of all dress;
wear only your nakedness.
O soul, priestess of nakedness,
the body is your temple.
O amber of the flesh
turn my hands to magnets,
and give me to drink
the Olympian nectar of nakedness.

Tear the veil,
throw away the robe,
and attune to nature
the living sculpture of your form.
Loosen the girdle; cross
your hands over the heart
and let your hair flow,
your long purple tresses.

Become a tranquil statue:
let your body take
the perfect form of art
that shines on the stone.
With your naked thoughts
play and imitate
the lithe beasts
the snakes and the birds.

And revel and follow
all the beautiful, pleasure-giving things;
elevate your nakedness
and make it a dream.
O round and smooth surfaces,
o lines and curves of skin—
divine shiverings—
come dance one dance.

O forehead, eyes, waves
of hair, thighs and loins
secret ravines, roses of love,
myrtles and hiding places,
limbs that lock and bind.
O hands, fountains of caress,
doves of desire,
hawks of destruction.

And let words rise from the heart
o mouth, o mouth,
like the sweet honey-comb,
the ripe pomegranate.
Even the alabaster lilies,
the censers of spring,
envy the full cups
of your breasts—o let me drink!

Let me drink from your rose-tipped
erect, glittering breasts
the milk that I dreamed,
the milk of happiness—you.
I am your mystic priest,
your knees are altars;
and in your burning arms
gods work their miracles.

Away from us all disharmonious things,
the clothed and hidden,
all defective and ugly things,
the unclean and unrevealed.
Only the naked and pure for us:
earth, skies, bodies, breasts.
For nakedness is truth,
and nakedness is beauty.

—And if in the sungraced nakedness
of the Athenian day
you thought you saw
something like a beast,
something like a leafless tree
without the shadow's grace,
like a rough stone or a dried-up body,

some naked creature
in the open spaces,
alive only
in its flaming eyes,
some descendant of Satyrs,
untamed
and silver-voiced—
Do not flee. It is I,

the Satyr. And I have taken roots
here like the olive tree,
stirring the winds of desire
with my deep-sounding reed.
I play and all things mate,
giving and receiving love;
I play and all things dance:
elements, beasts and men.

. . . .

Notes and References

Chapter One

1. For much of the material on Palamas's childhood and psychological development I am indebted to *Palamas—A Psychological Analysis of His Work and His Life* by the eminent psychiatrist Angelos Doxas. This work is indispensable for an understanding of the complex personality of Palamas.

2. The quoted translations from Palamas's *Life Immovable* are by Aristides Phoutrides. All other translations of verse and prose are the author's.

3. "My Years and My Papers," *Works*, IV, p. 307.

4. *Life Immovable:* "Fatherlands" II, "The Dead Youth," "A Hundred Voices" 15; *The Sorrows of the Lagoon:* "Delirium," and so on.

5. "My Years and My Papers," *Works*, IV, p. 305.

6. Quoted by a Doxas in *Palamas,* p. 53. There is not adequate space in this study to fully treat this aspect of Palamas's life, his sensuality. Suffice it to say here that the pattern of desire-adoration and "abandonment" of women continued throughout his life. Woman—flesh and idea, desire and idol—was a continuous haunting presence in his life, and consequently in his work.

7. K. Th. Dimaras, *History of Modern Greek Literature* (Athens, 1948), p. 22.

8. *Dionysius Solomos* (Cambridge, England, 1940), p. 59.

9. *Ibid.,* p. 16.

10. *Palamas and His Times* I, (Athens, 1944), pp. 46-47.

11. Quoted by Romilly Jenkins in *Dionysius Solomos,* p. 140.

12. *Palamas* (Athens, 1962) p. 196.

13. "My Poetics," *Works,* X, p. 520.

Chapter Two

1. "My Poetics," *Works,* X, p. 513.

2. *Ibid.,* p. 493.

3. *Ibid.,* p. 508.

4. *Ibid.*, p. 514.

5. K. Tsatsos, *Palamas* (Athens, 1949), p. 274.

6. *A Study of the Palm Tree of Kostis Palamas* (Athens, 1931).

7. Glafkos Alithersis, "The Palm Tree," *Nea Zoe*, XIII (1926), pp. 29-30.

8. "My Poetics," *Works*, X, p. 444.

9. L. Palamas, *A Study of the Palm Tree*, pp. 21-23.

10. *Ibid.*, p. 553.

11. Quoted by Hourmouzios in *Palamas and His Times*, I, pp. 176-77.

12. "My Poetics," *Works*, X, p. 523.

13. *Ibid.*, p. 553.

14. A. Phoutrides, *A Hundred Voices*, Introduction, p. 10.

15. *Palamas and His Times*, I, p. 195.

16. Quoted by Hourmouzios in *Palamas and His Times*, I, pp. 197-98.

17. "My Poetics," *Works*, X, p. 520.

18. A. Phoutrides, *A Hundred Voices* pp. 25-26.

19. "My Poetics," *Works*, X, pp. 520-21.

Chapter Three

1. "My Years and My Papers," *Works*, IV, p. 383.

2. "My Poetics," *Works*, X, p. 470.

3. There is direct reference in this part of the poem to the Neoplatonic philosopher Georgios Gemistos or Plethon (c. 1400) whose book *Laws* was burned by order of Patriarch Gennadios.

4. K. Tsatsos, *Palamas*, pp. 154-55.

5. *Kostis Palamas*, (Athens, 1943), p. 25.

6. Article by Petros Vlastos reprinted in K. Palamas, *The Dodecalogue of the Gypsy*, 4th ed. (Athens, 1950), p. 211.

7. V. Kouzopoulos, *The Dodecalogue of the Gypsy* (Athens, 1930).

8. D. Vezanis, *Palamas the Philosopher* (Athens, 1930), p. 144.

9. Alkis Thrylos, quoted by A. Karandonis in *About Palamas* (Athens, 1932), p. 143.

10. A. Karandonis, *About Palamas*, p. 149.

11. J. P. Anton, "Intellectual Forces in Modern Greek Poetry," *Athene*, XV (Autumn 1954), p. 90.

Chapter Four

1. "Prose Paths," *Works*, X, p. 15.

2. This line is derived from Goethe's *Faust*, Part II.

3. K. Tsatsos, *Palamas*, p. 164.

4. "My Poetics," *Works*, X, p. 417.

5. K. Tsatsos, *Palamas*, p. 164.

6. I. M. Panayotopoulos, *Palamas*, p. 193.

7. "My Poetics," *Works*, X, pp. 523-24.

8. K. Tsatsos, *Palamas*, p. 170.

9. E. Hourmouzios, *Palamas and His Times*, II (Athens, 1959), p. 282.

10. *Ibid.*, p. 284.

11. *Ibid.*, p. 288.

12. *Ibid.*, p. 290.

13. *Palamas, Kavafis, Sikelianos*, New Edition (Athens, n.d.), p. 118.

Chapter Five

1. "My Poetics," *Works*, X, p. 463.

2. *Works*, V, p. 287.

3. "My Poetics," *Works*, X, p. 531.

4. *Ibid.*, p. 545.

5. The poem was written after Palamas spent an evening with Venizelos at a friend's house at the time when Venizelos had resigned as prime minister in disagreement with King Constantine over the question of Greece's participation in World War I. Venizelos wanted immediate participation on the side of the Allies, while the pro-German Constantine was against it.

6. *Works*, VII, p. 177.

7. *Ibid.*, p. 179.

8. *Ibid.*, p. 440.

9. *Ibid.*, p. 443.

10. *Ibid.*, p. 446.

11. *About Palamas*, pp. 33-34.

12. One of the very few exceptions is the long poem "Homeric Hymn," written in 1935.

13. *Palamas and His Times*, III, p. 374.

14. *Op.cit.* p. 81.

15. *Palamas*, p. 248.

Chapter Six

1. Palamas, "The World of Letters," *Works*, VI, p. 21.

2. *Ibid.*, p. 193.

3. "Paths in Prose," X, pp. 65-66.

4. *Ibid.*, p. 219.

5. *Ibid.*, pp. 250-51.

6. *Ibid.*, p. 225.

7. *Ibid.*, p. 248.

8. *Ibid.*, pp. 85-86.

9. Palamas, Introduction to "Music Twice Tuned," *Works*, XI, p. 214.

10. *Ibid.,* p. 212.

11. Enid Starkie, *Les Sources du lyrisme dans la poésie d' Emile Verhaeren* (Paris, 1927), p. 319.

12. *Six French Poets* (New York, 1916), p. 47.

13. "Costis Palamas et l' Europe," *Revue de Littérature comparée* (July—September, 1947), pp. 380-81.

14. "Paths in Prose," *Works*, X, p. 142.

15. *Ibid.,* pp. 147-48.

16. *The Philosophy of Nietzsche* (New York, 1927), p. 56.

17. "Paths in Prose," X, P. 157.

18. "My Poetics," X, p. 492.

19. "Paths in Prose,. X, p. 91.

20. "Verses Mild and Harsh," IX, p. 127.

21. "My Poetics," *Works,* X, p. 479.

22. *Kostis Palamas,* p. 27.

23. "First Critical Essays" (Athens, 1913), p. 193.

24. "Paths in Prose," *Works,* X, p. 113.

25. "Poetic Art and Language," *Works,* VIII, p. 12.

Chapter Seven

1. *Dokimes,* pp. 44-45.

2. *Palamas, Kavafis, Sikelianos,* Introduction, pp. xiv-xv.

Selected Bibliography

PRIMARY SOURCES

Editions:

1. *Complete Works*

The first systematic and authoritative edition of the work of Palamas was undertaken by the Kostis Palamas Foundation in the early 1960's. Sixteen large volumes (of more than five hundred pages each) have appeared to date under the title APANTA (Complete Works). All references in this volume are to this edition.

2. *First Editions*

A. Poetry

Songs of My Country (Tragoudia tis Patridos mou). Athens: Hestia, 1886.

Hymn to Athena (Hymnos is tin Athenan). Athens: Hestia, 1889.

The Eyes of My Soul (Ta Matia tis Psychis mou). Athens: Hestia, 1892.

Iambs and Anapaests (Iamvi ke Anapesti). Athens: Hestia, 1897.

The Grave (O Taphos). Athens: Hestia, 1898.

Greetings to the Sunborn Woman (I Chairetismi tis Heliogennitis). Peiraeus: Editions *"To Periodiko mas,"* 1900.

Life Immovable (I Asalefti Zoe). Athens: Hestia, 1904.

The Dodecalogue of the Gypsy (O Dodekalogos tou Yyftou). Athens: Hestia, 1907.

The King's Flute (I Floyera tou Vasilia). Athens: Hestia, 1910.

The Sorrows of the Lagoon and The Satirical Exercises (I Kaimi tis Limnothalassas ke ta Satirika Gymnasmata). Athens: Fexis, 1912.

City and Solitude (I Politeia ke i Monaxia). Athens: Hestia, 1912.

The Altars (Vomi). Athens: Hestia, 1915.

Poems Out of Season(Ta Parakaira). Athens: I. N. Sideris, 1919.

Sonnets (Ta Dekatetrasticha). Alexandria: Editions *"Grammata".* 1919.

The Pentasyllabics and The Passionate Whispers (I Pentasyllavi ke ta Pathitika Kryfomilimata). Athens: I. D. Kollaros, 1925.

Verses Mild and Harsh (Thili ke Skliri Stichi). Chicago: Neohellenic Mercury, 1928.

The Cycle of the Quatrains (O Kyklos ton Tetrastichon). Athens:
    Editions "Korais," 1929.
Wanderings and Salutations (Perasmata ke Cheretismi). Athens: I. D.
    Kollaros, 1931.
The Nights of Phemios (1931–1932) (I Nychtes tou Phemiou). Athens:
    I. D. Kollaros, 1935.
*Evening Fire (Vrathini Fotia) [Posthumous poems edited by Leandros
    Palamas],* Athens: Hestia, 1944.

B. Criticism:
The Work of Krystallis (To Ergo tou Krystalli). Athens: Hestia, 1894.
The World of Letters, I (Grammata). Athens: Hestia, 1904.
The World of Letters, II (Grammata). Athens: Hestia, 1907.
The First Critical Essays (Ta Prota Kritika). Athens: Fexis, 1913.
Aristotelis Valaoritis. Athens: Hestia, 1914.
Paths in Prose, I & II (Pezi Dromi). Athens: Zikakis, 1928.
*My Years and My Papers I : My Poetics (Ta Chronia mou ke ta Chartia
    mou. I Poieteki mou)'* Athens: I. D. Kollaros, 1933.
Dionysios Solomos. Athens: Pyrsos, 1933.
Paths in Prose, III. Athens: P. Demetrakos, 1934.
My Years and My Papers, II. Athens: Hestia, 1940.

C. Short Stories:
A Man's Death (Thanatos Pallikariou). Athens: Hestia, 1901
Short Stories (Thiegimata). Athenes: I. N. Sideris [1920]

D. Drama:
Trisevgeni [The Thrice-noble Woman]. Athens: Hestia, 1903.

E. Translations:
Hélène de Sparte [Helen of Sparta] by Emile Verhaeren. Athens:
    Editions "Ta Erga," 1916.
Music Twice Tuned (Xanatonismeni Musiki). Athens: Hestia, 1930.

3.   *Translated Works of Palamas*
A. In French:
La Mort du Pallicare. Traduit par Jean d'Argos. Athènes: Editions du
    Monde Hellénique, 1907.
Oeuvres choisies, Tomes I & II. Traduites par Eugène Clément. Paris:
    Editions E. Sansot, [1922].
Le Tombeau. Traduction par Pierre Baudry. Athènes: Librairie
    Kauffman [1930].
Choix de Poésies. Traduction par Pierre Baudry. Athènes: Librairie
    Kauffman [1930].

Les Douzes Paroles du Tzigane. Traduit par Eugène Clément. Paris: Librairie Stock, 1931.

La Flute du Roi. Traduit par Eugène Clément. Paris: Librairie Stock, 1934.

B. In English:

Life Immovable. First Part. Translated by Aristides E. Phoutrides. Cambridge: Harvard University Press, 1919.

A Hundred Voices. Second Part of *Life Immovable.* Translated by Aristides E. Phoutrides. Cambridge: Harvard University Press, 1921.

Royal Blossom or Trisevyene. Translated by Aristides E. Phoutrides. New Haven: Yale University, 1923.

Poems. Selected and Rendered into English by Theodore Ph. Stephanides and George C. Katsimbalis. London: Hazell, Watson & Viney Ltd., 1925.

The Grave. Translated by Demetrios A. Michalaros. Chicago: The American Hellenic Book Co., 1930.

A Man's Death. Translated by A. E. Phoutrides. Athens: Hestia, 1934.

The Twelve Words of the Gypsy. Translated by Frederic Will. Lincoln: The University of Nebraska Press. 1964.

The King's Flute. Translated by Frederic Will. Lincoln: The University of Nebraska Press, 1967.

Three Poems ["The Palm Tree," "The Chains," "The Satyr or The Song of Nakedness."]. London: No publisher given. 1969.

The Twelve Lays of the Gipsy. Translated by George Thomson. London: Lawrence & Wishart, 1969.

SECONDARY SOURCES

ALITHERSIS, GLAUKOS. "The Palm Tree." *Nea Zoé,* XIII (1926) [Special issue on Palamas], 27-33.

ANTON, JOHN P. "Intellectual Forces in Greek Poetry." *Athene,* XV (Autumn 1954), 86-90.

Athene, IV (June, 1943). Special issue on "Palamas and His Period."

DIMARAS, C. TH. *Kostis Palamas.* Athens: Ikaros, 1947.

Grammata. December, 1943. Special issue on Palamas.

HOURMOUZIOS, EMILIOS. *Palamas and His Times,* I. Athens: Pegasos, 1944.

————., *Palamas and His Times,* II. Athens: Editions "Dionysos," 1959.

————., *Palamas and His Times,* III. Athens: Editions "Dionysos," 1960.

KARANDONIS, ANDREAS. *About Palamas*. Second Edition. Athens: Hestia, 1959.

KOUZOPOULOS, VASILIS. *The Dodecalogue of the Gypsy*. Athena: Hestia, 1930

MILLIEX, ROGER. "Costis Palamas et l'Europe." *Revue de Littérature comparée* (July–September, 1947), pp. 355-81.

MYRIVILIS, STRATIS. *Palamas in My Life*. Athens: Fexis, 1963.

Nea Hestia, XXXIV (December, 1943). Special issue on Palamas.

PALAMAS, LEANDROS. *A Study on the Palm-Tree of Kostes Palamas*, trans. into English by T. P. Stephanides and G. C. Katsimbalis. Athens: Hestia, 1931.

PANAYOTOPOULOS, I. M. *Palamas*. Second Editon, Athens: Fexis, 1962.

PAPANOUTSOS, E. P. *Palamas, Kavaphis, Sikelianos*. New Edition. Athena: Ikaros, [1955].

————. "Palamas the Thinker." *Paideia & Zoé*, III, Nos. 29-30, pp. 131-140, 163-173.

SEFERIS, GEORGE. "Kostis Palamas" in *Dokimes* (Essays), Second Edition. Athens: Fexis, 1962.

SHERRARD, PHILIP. "Costis Palamas" in *The Marble Threshing Floor-Studies in Modern Greek Poetry*. London: Vallentine, Mitchell, 1956.

SIKELIANOS, ANGELOS. *Kostis Palamas*. Athens: Alpha, 1943.

TSATSOS, CONSTANTINE. *Palamas*. Athens: Ikaros, 1949.

VEZANIS, DEMETRIOS. *Palamas as Philosopher*. Athens: Pallis, 1930.

ZACHARIADIS, NIKOS. *The True Palamas*. Athens: Ta Nea Biblia, 1945.

GENERAL SOURCES

BAUD-BOVY, SAMUEL. *Poésie de la Grèce moderne*. Lausanne: La Concorde, 1946.

DALVEN, RAE, ed. and trans. *Modern Greek Poetry*. New York: Gaer, 1949.

DESONAY, F. *La Rêve hellénique chez les poètes parnassiens*. Paris: Champion, 1928.

DIMARAS, C. TH. *History of Modern Greek Literature*. 2 vols. Athens: Ikaros, 1948.

FAIRLIE, ALISON. *Leconte de Lisle's Poems on the Barbarian Races*. Cambridge Mass: Univ. Press, 1947.

GRANT, ELLIOTT M., ed. *French Poetry of the Nineteenth Century*. New York: Macmillan, 1932.

HESSELING, D. C. *Histoire de la littérature grecque moderne*, trans. from the Dutch by H. Pernot. Paris: Société d'Edition Les Belles Lettres, 1924.

JENKINS, ROMILLY, *Dionysius Solomos.* Cambridge, England: Univ. Press, 1940.

KATSIMBALIS, G. K. *Bibliography of Kostis Palamas.* Athens: I. D. Kollanos, 1943.

KORDATOS, JOHN K. *The History of Our Language Question.* Athens: Loukatos, 1943.

LOWELL, AMY. *Six French Poets.* New York: Macmillan, 1916.

MOREAS, JEAN. *Les Stances.* 6th ed. Paris: Mercure de France, 1910.

NIETZSCHE, FRIEDRICH. *The Philosophy of Nietzsche.* The Modern Library. New York: Random House, 1927.

RAYMOND, MARCEL. *From Baudelaire to Surrealism.* New York: Wittenborn, Schultz, 1950.

SCHAFFER, AARON. *Parnassus in France.* Austin: Univ. of Texas, 1929.

SOLOMOS, DIONYSIOS. *Complete Works.* Athens: M. G. Vasileiou, 1936.

STARKIE, ENID. *Les Sources du lyrisme dans la poésie d'Emile Verhaeren.* Paris: E. De Boccard, 1927.

VERHAEREN, EMILE. *Les Villes tentaculaires.* 9th ed. Paris: Mercure de France, 1913.

Index

WHAT SADIE SANG

Story and pictures by Eve Rice

GREENWILLOW BOOKS . New York

Issued in new, larger format 1983.
10 9 8 7 6 5 4 3 2 1

Library of Congress Cataloging
in Publication Data

Rice, Eve.   What Sadie sang.

Summary: Even though Sadie's
song is only one syllable, it
means many things to her and her
mother as they go for a walk.
[1. Infants—Fiction]
1. Title. PZ7.R3622Wh [E]
75-33244   ISBN 0-688-80038-6
ISBN 0-688-84038-8 lib. bdg.
ISBN 0-688-02179-4 (1983 Printing)
ISBN 0-688-02181-6 (lib. bdg. : 1983 Printing)

Sadie could walk all by herself.

But today she did not want to walk.

So Mama put Sadie in her stroller.

"There," said Mama.

"Ooooh!" said Sadie.

Mama pushed.

The sticky stroller wheels

went click, click, click.

"Gheee!" said Sadie.

And "Gheee, gheee, gheee!"

"What is the matter?" asked Mrs. Finley.

"Is Sadie crying?"

But Sadie was not crying. She was singing.
And she sang "Gheee, gheee, gheee" again.

Sadie sang

to the tree on the corner

and to the red, red fire hydrant,

to a new spring tulip in a tub,

and to a scratching shaggy dog,

who said "Woof" in return.

"Gheee, gheee, gheee,"
all the way down the street.

And the grocer said,

"Maybe it's a toothache."

But Mama did not worry.

She knew a song when she heard one.

Sadie sang as they went to the river—

for the chugging tugboat

and the circling seagull.

Now "Gheee, gheee, gheee" was a river song.

Mama turned the stroller around
and Sadie kept right on singing,
so then it was a going-home song.

It was a very good going-home song
because Sadie was still singing
when Mama unlocked the front door.

"There," said Mama. "Naptime."

"Ummmm," said Sadie.

And she sang "Gheee, gheee, gheee"
all the way up the stairs

and into bed.

"Gheee, gheee, gheee," sang Sadie.

But that was the end of the song…

because Sadie was asleep.